Particles

Terry Hudson

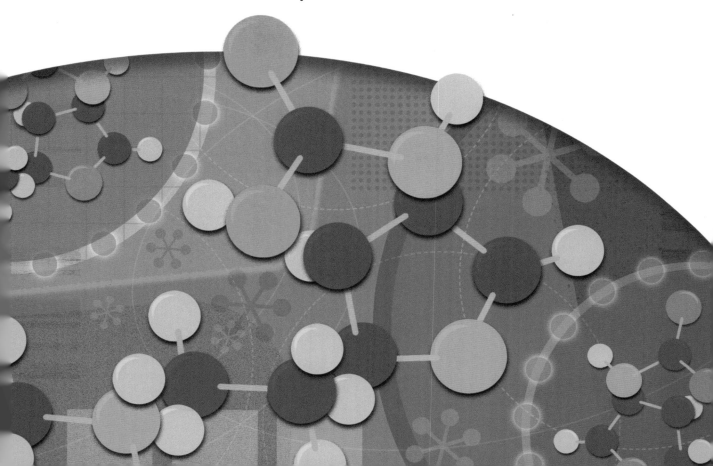

Framework objectives matched to material in this book

Teaching objective	Related chapters	Teaching objective	Related chapters
Y7 P1	Explaining the world around us, 2 Particle theory and the states of matter, 7 Heating and particles, 13	Y8 SE4	Particles and cells, 48 How atoms combine, 66
Y7 P2	Particle theory and the states of matter, 10 Heating and particles, 13 Expansion and contraction, 21 Particles that make up air, 27	Y8 SE5	Elements, mixtures and compounds, 59
		Y8 SE6	Spreading out, 38
		Y8 SE7	Elements, mixtures and compounds, 59
Y7 SE1	Explaining the world around us, 2	**Y9 P1**	Particles and chemical reactions, 74 Particles and energy, 79
Y7 SE2	Particle theory and the states of matter, 9	Y9 P2	Particles and chemical reactions, 74
Y7 SE3	Spreading out, 37	Y9 P3	Particles and chemical reactions, 74
Y7 SE4	Expansion and contraction, 25	Y9 P4	Atoms and patterns, 68
Y7 SE5	Particles that make up the air, 27 Spreading out, 38	Y9 P5	Atoms and patterns, 68
Y7 SE6	Expansion and contraction, 22 Spreading out, 38	**Y9 SE1**	Explaining the world around us, 2 The image of atoms, 84
		Y9 SE2	Spreading out, 34
Y7 SE7	Spreading out, 37	Y9 SE3	Spreading out, 34 Making crystals, 43 Elements, mixtures and compounds, 55
Y8 P1	Making crystals, 39 Particles and cells, 45		
Y8 P2	Atoms and Dalton, 50 Elements, mixtures and compounds, 55	Y9 SE4	Spreading out, 34 Making crystals, 43
Y8 P3	How atoms combine, 61	Y9 SE5	Making crystals, 43 The image of atoms, 85
Y8 SE1	Explaining the world around us, 2	Y9 SE6	Atoms and patterns, 69 Particles and energy, 80
Y8 SE2	Elements, mixtures and compounds, 59	Y9 SE7	Spreading out, 34
Y8 SE3	Spreading out, 38		

Contents

How to use this book

Key Ideas: Particles can be used as enrichment material to motivate and enthuse students following any KS3 science course.

The 15 chapters of stimulating, cross-curricular scientific accounts and activities include fascinating facts on such diverse subjects as removing tattoos, dioxins in barbecued food, kidney dialysis, building foundations under water, historical uses of laughing gas and the Great Fire of London.

Each chapter consists of: an introduction; texts and activities; a review; and a unit summary. The activities cover a range of learning styles and can be used as class or group assignments, or enrichment exercises for individual pupils. To help you select material for lessons covering particular topics and skills, the grid on the facing page links Framework objectives with the relevant chapters and page numbers. In the grid:

- P = Particles
- SE = Scientific Enquiry Sc1
- Objectives are numbered consecutively, following the same order as the Framework for Teaching Science.

Answers to closed activities appear on pages 90–92, and key words in the text are defined in an index and glossary on page 93.

Key to coloured panels in the chapters

- lab experiments and web search activities
- written and group discussion activities
- research, evidence and scientific developments boxes
- interesting facts boxes

Key to symbols in activities boxes

- lab activity
- hazard that may be encountered during an experiment
- literacy activity
- web search activity
- Sc1 practice activity
- numeracy activity
- ICT activity, e.g. PowerPoint, interactive whiteboard

Explaining the world around us

Introduction

In this chapter we look at some of the early ideas about the nature of matter.

- The Greeks had ideas about the nature of matter thousands of years ago.
- The first person to propose the atomic theory of matter was Leucippus, 2500 years ago.
- The word 'atom' is Greek.
- In 1808, John Dalton proved scientifically that atoms existed.

Write down your ideas about the following statements:
- You can walk through air but not through a table.
- You can pass your hand through air faster than through water.
- Sugar in cubes will spread out through a cup of tea.

 ook around you. You will see objects that are hard or soft, elastic or brittle, shiny or dull. You will also notice that some substances are solids, like your desk, some are liquids, like your drink, and some are gases, like the air you are breathing. But what are these quite different types of materials made of?

Today, we believe that all matter is made up of small particles called atoms – this is known as the atomic theory.

1 Work with a partner.

a Make a list of words and phrases that contain the word 'atom'.

b Show your list to another pair and compare your answers.

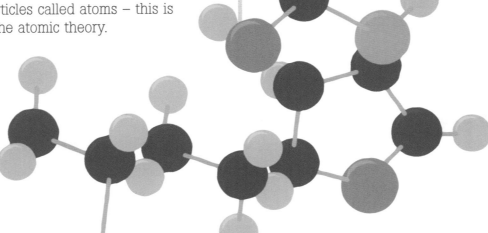

The Greeks develop the atomic theory

For thousands of years, scientists and philosophers have wondered about the nature of matter. Leucippus, living in Ancient Greece 2500 years ago, first proposed the idea that all matter is made up of particles.

Imagine the scene – Leucippus is sitting in the sunshine overlooking the sea and thinking about the materials around him. Perhaps he picks up a small lump of stone and holds it between his fingers. What would happen if the stone were cut in half? He would end up with two smaller pieces, of course. What would happen if these small pieces were cut in half, then in half again?

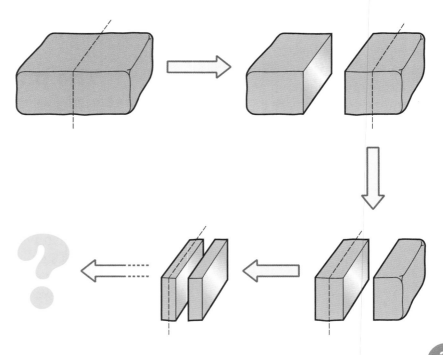

At the time, some philosophers thought that stone, and all other matter, could be cut in half – subdivided – again and again without limit. They said that however small the piece of stone became, it could always be split further. This didn't make sense to Leucippus. He believed that eventually you would arrive at a tiny particle of the stone that could not be split any further – a particle that could not be subdivided. Leucippus named such particles 'atoms'. He would have been pleased to know that his term is still used in our modern world.

> **2** Carry out the task below and then compare your drawing with a partner.
>
> **a** Look at the diagram on page 3 of a stone being cut in half several times.
>
> **b** Make your own drawings to show what you think will eventually happen if the stone is cut thousands of times. You will need to draw enlargements of the stone pieces when they get very small.

The student challenges the master

Leucippus had a very bright pupil whose name was Democritus. Both of these philosophers believed in atoms, but they disagreed over one very important point – the size of an atom.

In science, disagreements like this are common, and valuable because they prompt scientists to think carefully about their ideas and to gather evidence to support them. Only if ideas are challenged, tested and proved right can scientists be confident about them.

What was the disagreement?

Leucippus believed that a material could be broken down into atoms after only a few subdivisions. He regarded atoms as being fairly large – only just too small to be seen by the naked eye. Democritus, on the other hand, believed that it would take many subdivisions for matter to be subdivided to the atomic scale. He argued that atoms were in fact very, very small.

How small are atoms?

To give you some idea of the size of an atom, here are two amazing facts to think about:

- If you lined up 10 million atoms, the line would only be about 1 mm long!
- If this is not amazing enough, take a look at a ten pence piece. This small piece of material contains approximately 40 thousand, million, million, million atoms. No wonder they have been difficult to study and that many ideas about them have been put forward.

The phlogiston theory

In Ancient Greece, it wasn't possible to gather experimental evidence to prove the existence of atoms, so the idea of matter being made of tiny particles – atoms – was largely forgotten.

Over the centuries, other theories were suggested. One that gained particular attention was proposed in 1700 – the 'phlogiston' theory. It stated that there were three 'essences' that made up all matter. These were sulphur which helped burning, mercury which allowed materials to be fluid, and salt which gave materials stability. These 'essences' were thought to exist in different amounts in different materials, so giving them their different characteristics. Sulphur was renamed 'phlogiston' and was often known as the 'fiery principle'.

In the phlogiston theory, anything that burned (such as fuels) or that changed in the way that iron does when it rusts, was described as 'losing phlogiston'. Air was seen as somehow holding the phlogiston, helping things to burn.

This idea seems strange to us now, but it was widely believed at the time. It was brought into doubt by experimental evidence that showed, in fact, that metals increased in mass when they burned.

3 Work with a partner.

a Design and produce a poster that explains the phlogiston theory.

b Include the three 'essences' and what they were supposed to do.

c Prepare to explain the content of your poster to other pairs.

It was French scientist Lavoisier who finally put an end to the phlogiston theory. In one of his many contributions to science, he demonstrated that oxygen was needed for burning, rusting, and respiration and that, far from 'losing phlogiston', some materials gained mass during these processes. In a dramatic gesture, he burned many textbooks that supported the phlogiston theory. As well as explaining oxidation, Lavoisier is thought to have written the first chemistry textbook. Sadly, he was a victim of the French Revolution and was beheaded on the guillotine in 1794.

4 Work as a group to share ideas. Imagine you are going to interview Lavoisier.

a Write down six questions that you would ask him about his life and his discoveries.

b Swap questions with another group.

c Try to answer the questions you get by researching books and the internet, including the following:

http://www.chemheritage.org/
EducationalServices/chemach/fore/all.html

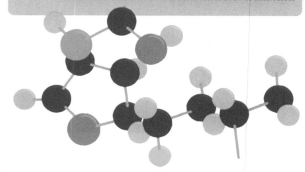

John Dalton and the rebirth of atomic theory

John Dalton, born in 1766, made many valuable contributions to science in his lifetime. He explained colour blindness (he was colour blind himself and for many years the condition was called Daltonism). He also studied atmosphere and gas pressures. But his most important contribution was to atomic theory. It was Dalton who first proved scientifically that atoms exist and can combine together in simple ratios to form new chemicals.

By this time, atoms were thought to be solid spheres like minute balls. (We can still use this model of atoms to explain the properties of solids, liquids and gases.) We now know that atoms themselves are made up of smaller, sub-atomic particles, but that is a story for a later chapter.

John Dalton.

5 Write a letter from John Dalton to Leucippus that explains Dalton's theory of atomic structure. Include some of the ways that our knowledge of atoms has enabled us to change our world.

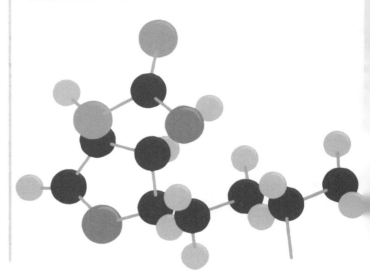

Review

John Dalton gave us the foundations of the atomic theory.

Work in a group. Select one person to read out the questions and then discuss the answers. Prepare to share your ideas with other groups.

- Which Greek philosopher first suggested that matter is made up of atoms?
- What was the argument between this philosopher and his student?
- How many atoms are needed to make a line roughly 1 mm long?
- Which scientist did the most to disprove the phlogiston theory?
- How did this scientist die?
- List three important scientific ideas proposed by John Dalton.

Chapter summary

In this chapter you have found out that:

- The Greek philosophers Leucippus and Democritus described the atomic theory 2500 years ago.
- Other theories of matter have existed, including the phlogiston theory.
- John Dalton showed scientifically that atoms exist and that they combine together to make other chemicals.

Particle theory and the states of matter

Introduction

In this chapter we look at the different states of matter and how we can explain their properties using particle theory.

- The three states of matter are solid, liquid and gas.
- Solids are hard, keep their shape and are difficult to compress or squash.
- Liquids take the shape of their container because they can flow.
- Gases have no fixed shape or volume and are easy to compress.
- In solids the particles are packed closely together, in liquids the particles are slightly less tightly packed than in solids, and in gases the particles are widely spaced.

Write down the names of five solids, five liquids and five gases.
For each one, describe its physical properties – what it looks and feels like - and what it is used for.

ll substances can be sorted into three groups: each substance is either a solid, a liquid or a gas. These are the three states of matter.

The way a substance feels, looks or behaves is called a property. It is clear that solids, liquids and gases do not look and feel the same. They also behave differently. The properties of solids, liquids and gases are shown in the table.

Property	Solid	Liquid	Gas
Volume	definite	definite	spreads to fill the container
Shape	definite	takes the shape of the lower part of the container	takes the whole container's shape
Density	very high	high	low
Ease of compression	very low	low	high
Ease of flow	nil	high	high

1 Work with a partner to decide whether the following materials are solids, liquids or gases.

a This material can be poured into a glass. It is not easy to compress and has a fixed volume.

b This material fills the whole room and is very easily compressed.

c This material will not pour and has a high density.

d This material takes the shape of the lower part of a container and is of medium density.

e This material has a high density and a fixed shape and volume.

The valuable properties of solids

Solids are made up of particles that are tightly packed together. These particles also hold on to each other very tightly, and although they do vibrate because of the energy they have due to temperature, they do not move about. All these properties mean that solids keep their shape and are often hard and durable (hard wearing). Because of this, solids are used to make strong structures like tall buildings, wide bridges, and hard-wearing roads, vehicles and furniture.

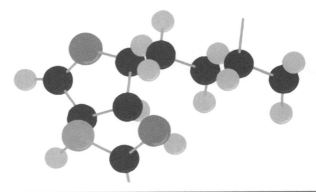

Solid

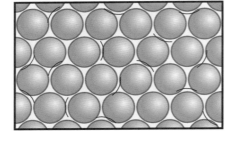

Liquid

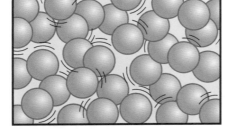

Gas

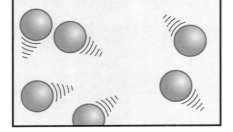

The Golden Gate Bridge, San Francisco. Such large bridges are possible only because of the properties of solids. The solid metal girders and cables create a very strong structure.

2 Work in a group to carry out the following tasks.

Your body contains solids, liquids and gases.

- Make a list of the solid parts of your body.
- Why is it important that these parts are made from solid substances?
- Write down what would happen if one of these parts turned to liquid.

3 You are going to construct a model bridge.

You will need:
- 30 strands of dry spaghetti
- sticky tape
- one piece of A4 card
- scissors
- ten 10 g masses

This is what you do:

1 Design and carefully construct a bridge using the spaghetti strands held together with sticky tape

2 The card will act as a roadway: you can cut the card into any lengths or as many pieces as you wish

3 Try to make your bridge as strong as possible: you will also gain points for the length of the bridge

4 Use some of the card to make a platform in the middle of the bridge so that the masses can be added when the bridge is tested

Once your bridge is complete, you should test it.

5 Place the bridge across a gap between two tables with only the ends of the bridge touching

6 Add 10 g masses to the platform until the bridge breaks. Be careful not to have your toes beneath the bridge!

Your group score will be the length of the bridge (in cm) multiplied by the mass it supported (in g). The group that gains the highest total of points is the winner.

Flowing liquids

Because the particles in a liquid are not quite so tightly packed as in a solid, they can move more easily. This is why liquids can flow.

Think back to the last drink you had from a glass. You may have noticed that the liquid was exactly the same shape as the glass. If you had poured it into a tall, thin glass, then the liquid would be a tall, thin shape; if you had poured it into a short, wide glass, the liquid would be a short, wide shape.

This is an important property of liquids. They flow and take the shape of their container. Notice that the volume stays the same. Unless you spill any of the liquid there will still be the same amount in each of the glasses.

Plasma – the fourth state

A fourth state of matter does exist. However, you are unlikely ever to see it as it only exists at the very high temperatures found inside stars, such as the Sun, in lightning flashes and during nuclear explosions. This state is called *plasma*. It consists of parts of atoms which have been broken up by electricity or extreme heat.

Advertising tricks

People who design the shapes of bottles for liquids such as perfumes and expensive drinks often try to make us think that we are getting more than we are. They know that if they put the liquid into a tall, thin bottle, there appears to be more than if they put it in a short, wide bottle. This is an optical illusion.

4 Work with a partner. When you have finished, share your ideas with another pair.

You will need:
- four different sized glass containers
- 100 cm³ measuring cylinder
- supply of tap water
- sink or place to pour away the water safely

This is what you do:

1 Collect your four different containers

2 Add exactly 50 cm³ of water to each container

3 Look at the containers and decide which one looks as if it contains the most liquid

4 Discuss your findings with another pair

Compressed gas cushions bumps

Gases are made up of particles that are widely spaced out and move freely. This means that gases can expand or contract to fill any space they are put into. Unlike solids or liquids, gases have no fixed shape or volume, and can easily be compressed.

Because gases have these properties, we are able to move easily through air. It is harder to move through liquids such as water, and we cannot move through solids such as a wall of bricks.

The fact that gases can be compressed makes them very useful. Car and bicycle tyres are filled with air so that when they pass over a bump, the air can be compressed and so cushion the bump. This gives a much smoother ride because the shock is absorbed.

5 Write down your ideas about the following tasks, and then compare them with a partner.

a Which property of gases is saving the stunt man in the photograph?

b What properties of concrete would make it more dangerous for the man to fall onto concrete from this height?

c Why would a fall onto concrete from a great height probably kill the man?

d List some other uses of gases.

e How are these uses linked to the properties of the gases?

A stunt man falls from a high building, but is unhurt!

Laughing gas

Nitrous oxide is a gas with a funny history. It has been used as an anaesthetic to put people to sleep during operations. However, it has also had other uses, as shown in the following extract.

   Laughing gas

Nitrous oxide is a colourless, almost odourless gas that was first discovered in 1793 by the English scientist and clergyman Joseph Priestley (who was also famous for being the first to isolate other important gases such as oxygen, carbon monoxide, carbon dioxide, ammonia, and sulphur dioxide). Priestley made N_2O by heating ammonium nitrate in the presence of iron filings, and then passing the gas that came off through water to remove toxic by-products.

After initial trials, Priestley thought that N_2O could be used as a preserving agent, but this proved unsuccessful.

Following Priestley's discovery, Humphry Davy of the Pneumatic Institute in Bristol experimented with the physiological properties of the gas, such as its effects upon respiration. He even administered the gas to visitors to the institute, and after watching the amusing effects on people who inhaled it, coined the term 'laughing gas'! Davy even noted the anaesthetic effects of the gas: 'As nitrous oxide in its extensive operation appears capable of destroying physical pain, it may probably be used with advantage during surgical operations in which no great effusion of blood takes place.'

However, despite this observation, for the next 40 years or so the primary use of N_2O was for recreational enjoyment and public shows. So-called nitrous oxide capers took place in travelling medicine shows and carnivals, where the public would pay a small amount to inhale a minute's worth of the gas. People would laugh and act silly until the effect of the drug came to its abrupt end, when they would stand about in confusion. Many famous people (of their time) and dignitaries from Clifton and Bristol came to inhale Davy's purified nitrous oxide for recreational purposes.

From an article by Ewan Cameron and Paul May, School of Chemistry, University of Bristol www.chm.bris.ac.uk/motm/n2o/n2oj.htm

6 Discuss the following questions with a partner and feed back to the class.

a Suggest how Priestley could have tested to see if nitrous oxide was a preservative.

b Why did Humphry Davy call nitrous oxide laughing gas?

c Why did Davy think nitrous oxide could be used during operations?

d Why is it very dangerous to breathe in gases other than air?

Review

Divide into teams. Each team discusses the questions and one person records the answers.

- ❏ What are the three states of matter?
- ❏ In which state are the particles closest together?
- ❏ In which state are the particles furthest apart?
- ❏ Explain why the air in a tyre acts as a shock absorber.
- ❏ Why does water take the shape of a cup, while the cup retains its shape?

Chapter summary

In this chapter you have found out that:

- ❏ The three states of matter are solid, liquid and gas.
- ❏ In solids the particles are packed closely together and hold on to each other very tightly.
- ❏ In liquids the particles are slightly less tightly packed and can move more easily.
- ❏ In gases the particles are widely spaced and move at great speeds.
- ❏ The arrangement of particles in solids, liquids and gases explains their properties.

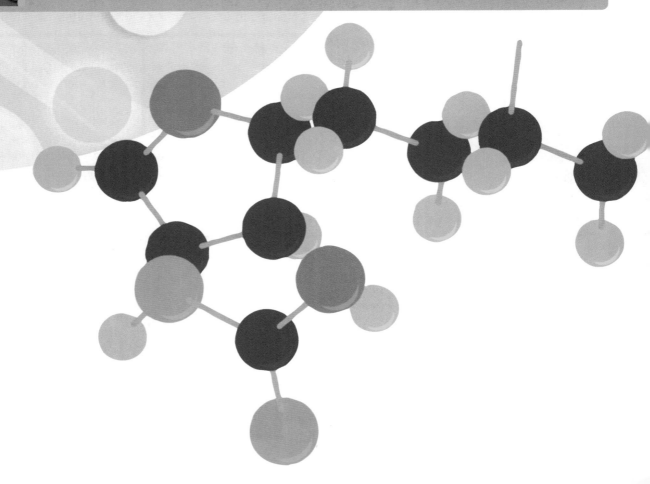

Heating and particles

Introduction

In this chapter, we look at what happens to particles as substances are heated.

- Changes of state depend on how close particles are in a substance, and how quickly they are moving.
- The change from solid to liquid is called melting.
- The change from liquid to gas is called evaporation.
- Gases condense to form liquids and liquids freeze to form solids.
- We can cause changes of state by changing the temperature of a substance.

Take two minutes to write down the different states of water you might see as you:
- make breakfast
- walk to school on a very cold day
- make a cup of coffee when you get home
- take some food out of the freezer.

The person in the photograph is taking a sample of liquid (molten) iron. The temperature of the iron is over 1500 °C. Iron is used to make steel, a solid used in structures such as bridges and buildings.

The state of a substance depends on how well ordered its particles are, and whether they are free to move independently. We can make a substance change state by changing its temperature. In the case of iron, it takes a huge input of heat energy to change from a solid to a liquid. The heat energy disrupts the forces that bind the particles together in the solid state. On melting, the particles become less well organised, and can move more freely.

These are two important things that happen as a substance melts:

- Energy added to the substance breaks the forces of attraction between the particles.
- The particles become less well ordered.

1 Write your own answers and then compare them with a partner.

  a How would the person in the photograph change the liquid (molten) iron back to a solid?

  b Why is the person not using a plastic ladle?

  c What do you think would happen to an ice cube if it were slowly moved towards the molten iron?

2 You are going to investigate the temperature of ice over five minutes.

You will need: 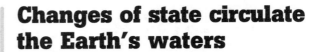 Wear safety goggles
  • safety goggles
  • 250 cm³ glass beaker
  • −10 to 110 °C thermometer, or temperature sensor
  • ice cubes
  • timer
  • graph paper

This is what you do:

1 Half fill the beaker with ice cubes

2 Take the temperature of the ice and record it

3 Record the temperature of the ice every 30 seconds for five minutes and record your observations

4 Draw a graph of your data

• Describe all of the changes that you see during the experiment, and anything that you have learned from your graph.

• Describe what you think is happening to the particles of the ice during the experiment.

Changes of state circulate the Earth's waters

Melting is not the only example of a change of state. The water in a puddle will seem to disappear as the Sun warms it. This is because the water has changed to water vapour. This change from a liquid to a gas is called evaporation. Without evaporation, it would not be possible to dry clothes. More importantly, we would not have the world's weather system. It is the evaporation of water from rivers, lakes and in particular the oceans that eventually causes clouds to form and the rain to fall that supplies these bodies of water. This circulation of water is called the water cycle (see diagram opposite).

Ice to the Equator?

Huge areas of the world are very short of drinking water, because the climate is very hot and dry, or because little or no rain falls. There are many ideas on how to supply water to these parts, and one idea that has been seriously suggested is to move frozen water from near the North Pole to desert regions just north of the Equator.

The frozen water in an iceberg is fresh water from snow, not seawater. The idea is for ships to tow huge icebergs from the Arctic to where the water is needed. It has been calculated that, although some ice would melt as it moves south, there would be plenty left to make the exercise worthwhile.

However, this idea has not been tried yet because of cost and hazards to shipping. There may also be other, cheaper ways of obtaining water, such as using the Sun's energy to evaporate drinking water from seawater in solar-powered desalination plants.

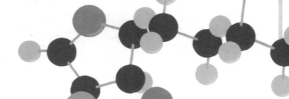

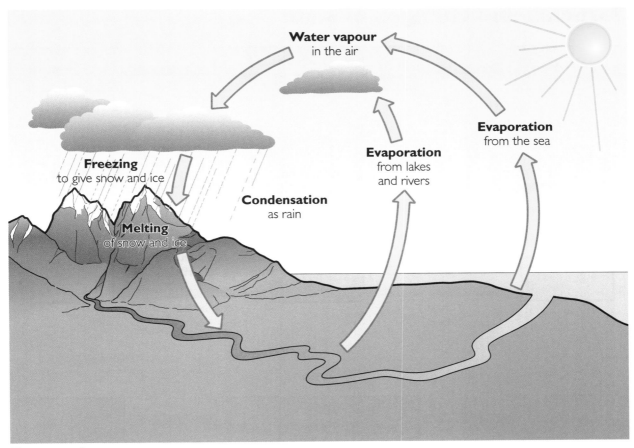

The water cycle.

Steam power

When water is heated, it changes to steam. In steam, the particles are further apart and moving more vigorously than in water. The steam that is produced takes up more space and has more energy than the water it is formed from. If you have watched a covered saucepan of boiling water, you may have noticed that energy in the steam can lift the lid up. James Watt noticed this, and was one of the first people to design a machine that uses this energy – the steam engine.

3 Work with a partner to carry out internet research on the following headings. Record the information you find and any useful web addresses.

Prepare a short presentation about your most interesting findings. You may wish to include printouts in your presentation.

- the life of James Watt
- the development of the steam engine
- the steam age
- uses of steam power today

Particles and changes of state

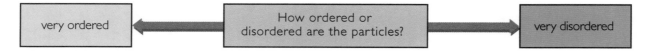

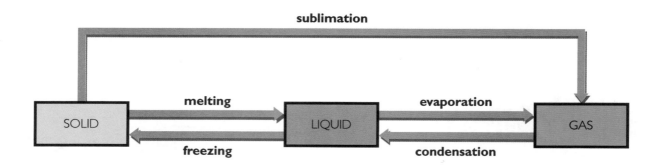

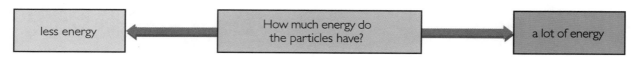

Changes of state and energy.

Note from the diagram that changes of state occur in two directions. These are from solid through liquid to gas, and from gas through liquid to solid. It is vital to realise that both these directions involve energy changes.

- To move from solid to liquid to gas requires energy to be added. The substance must be heated.
- To move from gas to liquid to solid requires energy to be removed. The substance must be cooled.

Where does the energy come from and go to during these changes? The answer is that the energy comes from or goes to the surroundings. If we imagine the change taking place inside a box, then everything inside the box is called the system. Everything outside the box is called the surroundings.

- When energy moves from the system to the surroundings, then the system will cool and the changes of state will involve condensation and freezing. The surroundings will become warmer.
- When energy moves from the surroundings to the system, then the system will warm up and the changes of state will involve evaporation and melting. The surroundings will become cooler.

Air conditioning

Air conditioning in houses and cars uses the idea that there are energy changes when substances change state. The main ingredient of air conditioning systems is a substance that easily changes from a liquid to a gas and back to a liquid again. This liquid is called freon.

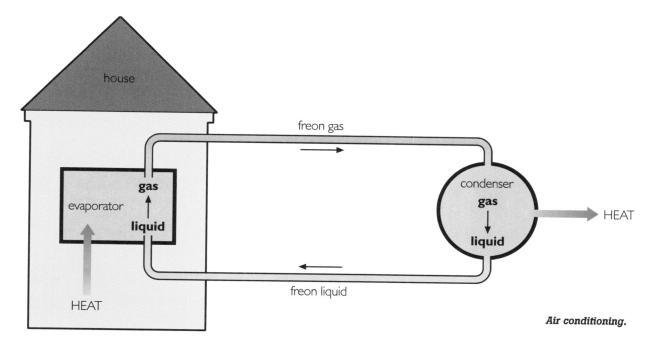

Air conditioning.

As the diagram shows, in the evaporator the freon changes from a liquid to a gas. For this change, the liquid must be provided with heat, and the heat comes from the room in the house. This makes the room cooler. Then, as a gas, the freon leaves the unit in the room to the condenser outside the building where it is condensed back into a liquid. In this process, the freon gives up heat energy to the surroundings. The freon is pumped round the system continuously; each time, heat is moved to the outside world.

---

4 Write down your answers and compare them with those of a partner's.

a Where in an air conditioner does a liquid change to a gas?

b Where in an air conditioner does a gas change to a liquid?

c Why does a room become cooler when an air conditioner is turned on?

d Draw a diagram to show what is happening to the freon particles as they move around the air conditioning system.

Heating curves

It is possible to follow the temperature of substances as they pass through the three different states. This is most easily done with water.

Ice is added to a beaker and slowly warmed using a Bunsen burner. The temperature is taken every 30 seconds. The ice melts. Then the liquid water is heated until eventually the water changes to water vapour.

The results of such an experiment are shown in the graph on the next page.

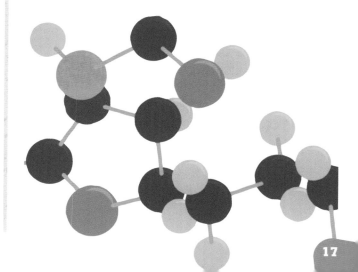

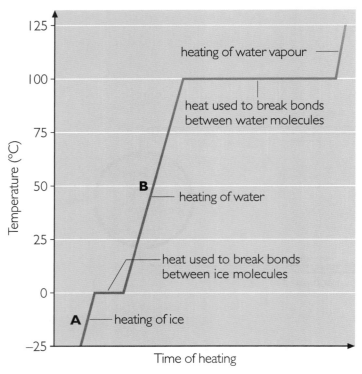

The heating curve for water, with energy supplied at a constant rate.

5 Working with a partner, answer these questions. Share your answers with another pair.

a Explain why the water does not immediately become any hotter once it reaches 100 °C.

b Produce your own version of the heating curve, adding diagrams to show what is happening to the particles as the water is heated.

There are some very interesting sections of the graph.

● During section A, the ice is being heated (energy is being transferred to it) but it has not yet changed state. The ice is getting warmer, recorded as a temperature increase.

● During section B, the water is being heated but it has not yet changed state. The water is getting warmer.

● Notice two 'flat' regions of the graph. One is at 0 °C. At this point the ice is starting to change state. The heat energy that is being added is breaking down the forces that hold the particles in fixed positions. The ice does not become warmer – there is no temperature increase. Eventually, the forces are overcome, the particles have enough energy to move free of their neighbours, and the ice melts.

Superheated steam

You have learnt that when water is boiled it turns to steam at 100 °C. If this steam passes through steel wool, nothing happens. However, it is possible to raise steam to a higher temperature at which it will react with steel wool. When steam is heated under pressure, its temperature rises – it is superheated. When it reaches 180 °C and is then passed through steel wool, the steam and steel react together and the steel wool is seen to glow.

This reaction has to be taken into account where steam is used for generating electricity. The hotter the steam, the more energy it has. Therefore, the more efficiently it will generate electricity (energy of the steam turns a turbine which converts the energy to electrical energy). However, the superheated steam travels through a lot of steel pipes, so it is essential to ensure that the steam does not get so hot that the pipes react with it. The people who control electricity generators need to balance up using steam that is hot enough to work efficiently, yet not so hot that it reacts with the pipes.

6 Write down your answers and then compare them with those of a partner.

   a Why is superheated steam more dangerous than steam out of the kettle?

   b How can superheated steam be made?

   c Describe some problems that could be caused by superheated steam.

Changes of state and poetry

The words used to define changes of state can also be used to describe feelings. Words such as boiling and melting are given new meanings. For example, you may have heard these phrases:

● It made my blood boil!

● His heart melted.

Poets, novelists and songwriters use such word to convey emotions.

7 Work with a partner.

   a Make a list of the words used to describe changes of state.

   b For each word, make up a sentence that uses the word and which describes your feelings or thoughts about something.

   c Share your ideas with another pair.

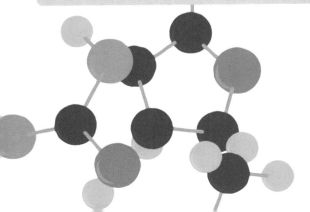

(The final entry of an ice cube's diary)

Melting point
From my chilly abode
I am removed
Brought out
Into an alien world
Unaccustomed
To these surroundings,
I suffer
Dying away,
Bit by bit,
Drop by drop,
The longer I stay, the more I die,
Slowly away.
From a strong
and solid
individual
I have become
Nothing but
a helpless,
shapeless
Soul.

(The Young Writer's Club member's Poems
No. 15232, Chubilicious May 22, 2003)

8 Work on your own to answer the questions.

   a What was the chilly abode mentioned in the poem?

   b Why were the phrases 'bit by bit' and 'drop by drop' used?

   c What state does the phrase 'helpless, shapeless soul' describe, and why?

9 Now write your own poem. Select one of the words that describe a change of state as your theme.

Read out your finished poem to a partner and then write a neat version so that it can be displayed.

Review

Divide the class into two teams. As a team, write down the answers to the questions. Each correct answer gains one point. The team with the higher score wins.

- Apart from solids and gases, what is the other state of matter?
- What happens to the particles in a solid when it is heated?
- What is the name of the process in which a liquid turns to a solid?
- When solids turn into liquids there is an increase in the level of disorder. True or false?
- Describe one problem caused by superheated steam.
- Name the substance used in air conditioning systems.

Chapter summary

In this chapter you have found out that:

- Substances can exist as solids, liquids and gases and that these are the three states of matter.
- The change from solid to liquid is called melting.
- The change from liquid to gas is called evaporation.
- The change from gas to liquid is called condensation.
- The change from liquid to solid is called freezing.
- The change from solid to liquid to gas requires heat energy to be added and leads to a state of greater disorder.
- The change from gas to liquid to solid requires loss of heat energy (cooling).

Expansion and contraction

Introduction

In this chapter we look at some of the effects of heating and cooling substances.

- When a solid is heated it expands because its particles vibrate faster and take up extra space.
- Liquids expand slightly more than solids, but a lot less than gases.
- When substances are cooled they contract.
- Expansion and contraction have many uses, but can also cause problems.

Work with a partner. You will need a plain piece of A4 paper, a 5p coin and a pencil.

- Draw a square in the middle of the paper, with sides 12 cm long.
- Label the square 'cold metal'.
- A 5 pence piece represents a particle of metal. Work out how many 5 pence pieces will fit into the cold metal square if they are arranged just touching each other and side by side. You can do this by just drawing round the coin over and over again.
- To represent 'hot metal', the 5 pence pieces must have a 1 mm gap between them. If you use the same number of 5 pence pieces, how big would a 'hot metal' square be?

You may not have realised it, but you have probably seen many examples of expansion and contraction. Every time you have had your temperature taken with a thermometer, you have seen expansion and contraction. The liquid inside the thermometer expands when heated and contracts when it cools. The more it is heated the more it expands.

For an explanation of expansion and contraction we have to think back to our particle model of matter. The more heat energy the particles have, the more vigorously they move around. This means they take up more space.

- In solids, the particles are held together firmly – they remain with their neighbours – and they do not move apart very far.
- In liquids, the particles are less tightly held – they can move past each other – and so liquids can expand more than solids.
- Gas particles are not held together tightly at all, and so gases expand a great deal more than liquids or solids.

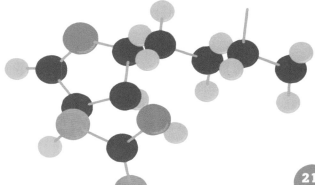

Getting bigger

Though metals and other solids expand less than liquids, and far less than gases, their expansion is still important. Expansion can result in tremendous forces. These forces are enough to buckle metal or shatter concrete and rock.

Designers and builders allow for the expansion of metals when they plan and build bridges, buildings and roads. Small gaps are left between sections so that, when the temperature increases, the solids have room to expand. These are called expansion joints (filled with compressible, rubbery material) or expansion gaps.

Not all solids are the same

Given the same input of heat energy, not all solids will expand by the same amount. Some materials will expand by a relatively large amount, while others hardly become much bigger. The amount a material expands is called its expansion.

Brass is an example of a solid that has a relatively high expansion. If you heat a 100 m length of brass by 10 °C it will expand by 19 mm. This may not seem much, but if this brass had to fit exactly into a machine or complicated structure, after a little heating an exact fit would be impossible. On the other hand, if you raise the temperature of a 100 m strip of oven glass by 10 °C, it will only expand by 3 mm.

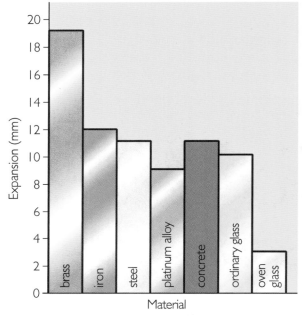

Expansion of solids: How much a 100 metre length of the material expands if heated by 10 °C.

1 Work with a partner to answer the questions, and then prepare to discuss them with others. You will need to study the chart to find some of the answers.

a Which solid expands the most?

b Which solid expands the least?

c Why is oven glass more useful in the kitchen than normal glass?

d Give one reason why using steel reinforcing rods in concrete would cause fewer problems than using brass rods during hot weather.

You may have seen this demonstration performed. The brass sphere will easily fit through the hoop when it is cool. After heating it is a different size. The brass sphere no longer fits through, no matter how it is turned – it wedges on top.

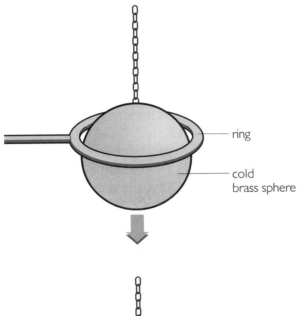

ring

cold
brass sphere

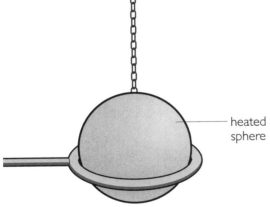

heated
sphere

2 Study the diagram with a partner.

a Why does the hot brass sphere not fit through the hoop?

b How does this demonstration show that expansion occurs?

c Draw how you think the particles are arranged in the cold brass sphere and the hot brass sphere.

Using expansion to measure temperature

The most common way to measure the temperature of a substance is to use a liquid-filled thermometer. Liquids commonly used in thermometers are alcohol and mercury.

Alcohol	Mercury
sticks to the glass and may not be accurate	expands easily, does not stick to glass and is accurate
low boiling point (78 °C) and low freezing point (−110 °C) takes time to warm up	high boiling point (360 °C) and high freezing point (−37 °C) warms up quickly
cheap	expensive
needs to be coloured	easy to see
not very toxic	very toxic

Advantages and disadvantages of alcohol and mercury thermometers.

3 Work with a partner to answer the questions.

a Which type of thermometer would be safer for taking body temperature readings?

b Why are mercury thermometers more accurate?

c Why would both thermometers be useless for taking the temperature of molten steel?

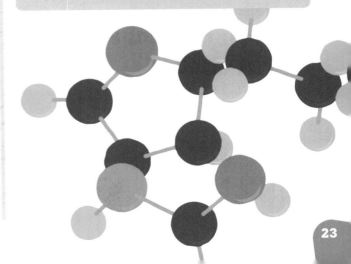

The unusual behaviour of water

Water acts in an unusual way when it is heated. As water is warmed up between 0 °C and 4 °C, the volume of the water actually falls. The water contracts rather than expands. Once heated above 4 °C, the water expands like other liquids. This means that the particles – molecules – of water are closest together at 4 °C, and that water takes up the least space at this temperature. Therefore water has its greatest density at this temperature. Water at 4 °C will sink down through both warmer and colder water, which are less dense!

A thermostat uses a bimetallic strip

The bimetallic strip is a clever invention. It is two strips of different metals – usually brass and iron – joined together. As you know from page 22, brass expands more than iron. When the bimetallic strip is heated, the brass expands more and this make the strip bend into a curve. This bending can be used to switch off an electrical circuit.

One application is in regulating the temperature in a room. Once the desired temperature is reached, the bimetallic strip bends and breaks the electrical contact of a heating system. This turns the heating off.

Celsius, Fahrenheit and Kelvin

You may still hear weather presenters and older people talking about the temperature on a very hot, sunny day as being 'in the 90s'. This measurement must be in degrees Fahrenheit. If it was in the Celsius range we use in science, then it would be almost as hot as boiling water! The following are the scales, and who invented them.

- The Fahrenheit scale was first developed by the German scientist Gabriel Daniel Fahrenheit (1686–1736). On the Fahrenheit scale the temperature of melting ice is 32 °F and boiling water is 212 °F. This scale is never used for scientific work.

- A professor of astronomy in Sweden, Anders Celsius (1701–1744) realised that it would be much easier if there were only 100 degrees between the melting point and the boiling point of water. The Celsius scale was born.

- The Kelvin scale, named after William Thompson, Lord Kelvin (1824–1907), is a scale commonly used in science. It has units that are the same size as Celsius degrees but the lowest value in Kelvin (0 K) is the same as –273 °C! This temperature, known as absolute zero, is the lowest possible temperature that material can theoretically reach – at which particles have no heat energy whatsoever.

4 Collect some newspaper cuttings that show the weather forecasts and some temperatures around the world. Select ten of the temperatures and present them in degrees Celsius, Fahrenheit and Kelvin.

- To convert from Celsius to Kelvin you subtract 273 degrees.

- To approximately convert from Celsius to Fahrenheit you double it and then add 32 degrees.

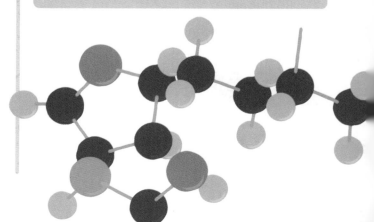

Expanding gases

5 Write your own answers and then share them with a partner.

   a List some ways that we use the expansion of gases.

   b What are some of the dangers and problems of gases when they expand?

   c Use the particle model to explain why gases expand more than solids and liquids.

6 You are going to explore the expansion of gases in the air.

You will need:
- 250 cm³ conical flask
- food colouring
- cork with glass tubing through it
- water

This is what you do:

1 Add 100 cm³ of water to the conical flask

2 Add a few drops of food colouring to the water

3 Carefully place the cork with the tubing into the conical flask so that the tube is below the water level; do this carefully and never press on to the glass tubing

4 Observe how far up the tube the coloured water is

5 Hold the conical flask in your hands to warm it

6 Observe what happens to the level of the coloured liquid in the tube

In activity 6 the flask was less than half full of the coloured water. This left plenty of room for air. As the flask was warmed in your hands the air expanded, and pushed the water further up the tube. This experiment shows just how quickly, and how much, gases expand.

7 Work with a partner to produce a leaflet describing one of the uses of expansion and contraction. You can use books or the internet to find out the information. Select one of the following topics:
- Making barrels
- Making wagon wheels
- Rivets
- Expansion gaps in roads and railway lines
- Dentists using fillings that expand at the same rate as the growing tooth
- Bimetallic strips in car indicators

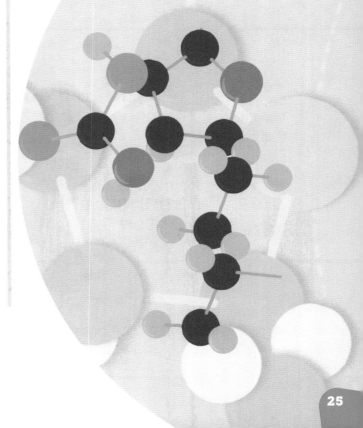

Review

Work in a group. Try to answer the following questions. Each group takes it in turn to read out their answers.

- ❏ With the same energy input, which expand more, solids or liquids?
- ❏ Gases expand 100 times more than solids. True or false?
- ❏ How is expansion used in thermometers?
- ❏ Do all solids expand the same amount and at the same rate?
- ❏ Describe what a bimetallic strip is and give one example of how it is used.
- ❏ Explain what happens to the particles of a gas as it expands.
- ❏ Give two uses of expansion and two problems caused by expansion.

Chapter summary

In this chapter you have found out that:

- ❏ When any substance is heated, the particles move further apart and the substance expands.
- ❏ Liquids expand more than solids, and gases expand more than liquids.
- ❏ Expansion and contraction are used in thermometers.

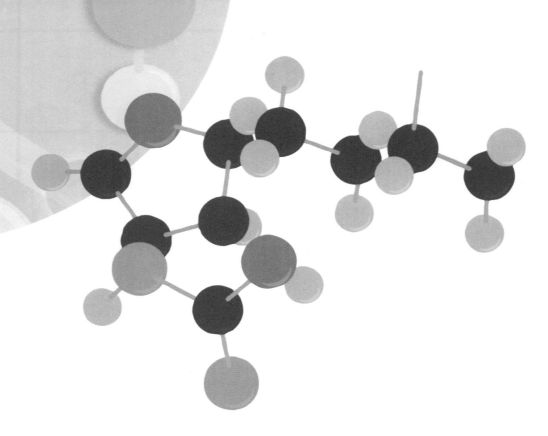

Particles that make up air

Introduction

In this chapter we look at the nature of air and the causes and effects of air pressure.

- ❏ Air is a mixture of gases.
- ❏ The layer of air that surrounds the Earth is called the atmosphere.
- ❏ The air in the atmosphere exerts a force on objects. This pressure is called atmospheric pressure or air pressure.
- ❏ The standard value of air pressure at the surface of the Earth varies from place to place and also depends on the weather.
- ❏ Air pressure can be very useful, but it also causes problems.

Air is a mixture of gases. Work with a partner to make a list of the gases you know to be in the air, and the reasons why they are important. Prepare to share your ideas with the class.

We live surrounded by air. This air forms a layer around the Earth that reaches hundreds of kilometres into space. However, most of the air is within 10 km of the Earth's surface. The atmosphere becomes thinner as you move from sea level, and this is why mountaineers find it difficult to breathe on very high mountains.

The particles of air are moving around in all directions at great speeds. This is often described as random and rapid motion. When the particles hit an object they exert a force. The more collisions there are between air particles and an object, the more force there will be. The particles hitting objects in this way cause air pressure.

1 The particles in air have weight. Work with a partner to investigate this.

You will need:
- string
- 1 m of dowel or bamboo cane
- 4 identical balloons
- narrow table or desk
- 2 equal-sized wooden blocks
- flat-sided pencil
- measuring tape

This is what you do:

1 Use tape to mark the middle of the dowel

2 Blow up two of the balloons so that they are equal in size

3 Tie a short piece of string to each balloon

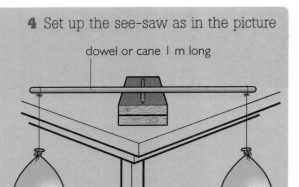

4 Set up the see-saw as in the picture

dowel or cane 1 m long

5 Hook one balloon to each end of the dowel

6 Let the see-saw settle and record what you see

7 Now blow up one of the remaining balloons so it is much bigger than the first two

8 Replace one of the original balloons on the dowel and let it settle

9 Record what happens

10 Finally, blow up the fourth balloon so that it is much smaller than the others. Replace the large balloon with this smaller balloon and let the see-saw settle

- What does this experiment tell you about the weight of air?
- Use diagrams to explain why some balloons are heavier than others.

Air pressure

The pressure caused by the particles in the air acts in all directions. Near the surface of the Earth, that pressure is at its maximum since there is so much atmosphere above us. The pressure is the same as ten cars pressing down on us – that is 100 000 pascals.

A pascal is one newton per square metre. The pascal is named after Blaise Pascal (1623–1662), a French scientist who was regarded as a genius, even as a boy. One of Pascal's experiments was to carry a barometer up a high mountain. He showed that air pressure falls with increasing height. Though Pascal was a great scientist, it is worth noting that calculating pressure was known about in China hundreds of years before Pascal was born.

The reason our lungs do not become crushed by air pressure is that the air inside them is at the same high pressure as the air all around us. If high-pressure air is outside an object and not inside it, then that can result in crushing damage.

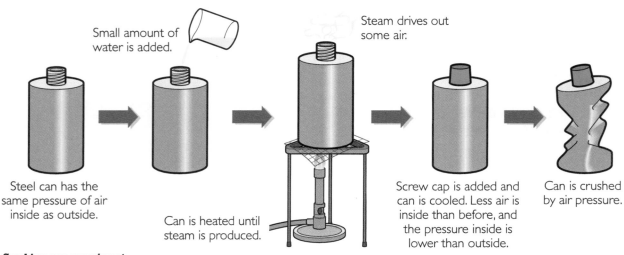

Small amount of water is added.

Steam drives out some air.

Steel can has the same pressure of air inside as outside.

Can is heated until steam is produced.

Screw cap is added and can is cooled. Less air is inside than before, and the pressure inside is lower than outside.

Can is crushed by air pressure.

Crushing can experiment.

Air pressure exceeds 16 horsepower

In 1656, Otto von Guericke arranged a fantastic demonstration in a town called Magdeburg. He pushed together two large metal hemispheres to make a giant ball. The only thing holding them together was a layer of grease, and they could be slid apart easily.

Next, using a modified pump, he removed the air from the two joined hemispheres. Now a person could not pull them apart. In fact, Otto von Guericke ordered that a team of eight horses be hitched to each hemisphere. They still couldn't pull them apart!

For centuries, scientists had debated whether it was possible to create a vacuum - a space that contained no particles. Many thought it was impossible, and the phrase 'nature abhors a vacuum' described their belief. Otto von Guericke showed with his experiment that a vacuum could exist and that the pressure of air particles on the outside of the hemispheres was a very powerful force.

Flying high

Air travellers to get better view

Cracked and unclear airplane windows will soon be a thing of the past due to a flexible, water-resistant polymer coating developed by Australian scientists.

The technology has been developed by CSIRO scientists and Aeroclear Pty Ltd, an Australian company specialising in the re-cutting of airplane windows.

The new polymer coating maintains a constant water content in the plastic of the window, preventing the frequent changes associated with changing air pressure which cause the plastic to crack.

'Previous attempts to develop a water-resistant coating have failed to reduce moisture loss due to their insufficient flexibility,' said Aeroclear's Geoff Thomas, 'A water-resistant coating is only useful so long as it doesn't crack.'

'Air pressure within the cabin is constant, yet changing altitude causes outside air pressure to fluctuate. As a result of the difference in pressure, airplane windows change shape throughout a flight and, in the past, this has caused the coating to crack,' he said.

As well as benefiting the passenger, Mr Thomas predicts the thinner, more flexible polymer will result in massive cost savings for airlines. Currently aircraft are taken out of service every three years to remove and re-cut windows.

Extract from 'News in Science', Wednesday 31 May 2000
www.abc.net.au/science/news/stories/s132484.htm

2 Discuss the following questions with a partner, then write down your ideas. Prepare to share your ideas with others.

  a Why must the air pressure inside the cabin of an aircraft be kept constant as far as possible?

  b What happens to the air pressure outside the airplane as it flies higher?

  c Why does this cause the airplane windows to change shape?

  d The cabin air pressure does change slightly on takeoff and landing. Why does this cause some people to have pain in their ears?

Measuring air pressure

The instruments we use to measure air pressure are called barometers.

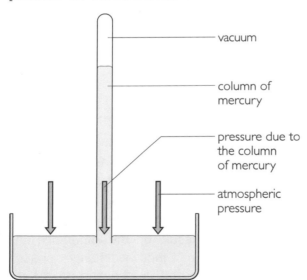

- vacuum
- column of mercury
- pressure due to the column of mercury
- atmospheric pressure

As shown in the diagram, the simplest type of barometer consists of a long, straight glass tube sealed at one end and containing the liquid mercury. It is placed, sealed end upwards, in a trough of mercury. The downward pressure of air on the mercury in the trough equals the pressure of the mass of the column of mercury. In this way the mercury stays up the tube, leaving a vacuum

at the sealed, top end. As the air pressure increases, the mercury in the tube rises. As air pressure falls, the mercury in the tube falls. The height of mercury in the tube can therefore be used to measure air pressure.

Mercury is a toxic chemical and so another type of barometer, an aneroid barometer, is very common (aneroid means liquid free). It consists of a sealed metal circular box from which most of the air has been removed, so that it contains a near-vacuum. A rotating pointer is attached to the box on a clock face marked in units of pressure. As air pressure rises, it compresses the box, and the needle turns to show how much the air pressure has changed. If the air pressure then drops, the box expands a little, and the needle turns the other way.

Weather maps and isobars

The pressure of the atmosphere can be mapped: as with mapping atmospheric temperatures, all the places with the same air pressure can be joined together. This gives a line showing positions of equal pressure, called an isobar. Weather forecasters can predict the weather by studying the patterns of these isobars.

3 In a group, use books or the internet to research the following things about air pressure and the weather. Then give a short presentation to the class.

  a What is meant by a depression? What weather does it usually bring?

  b What type of weather would you expect if there was high pressure in winter?

  c What is a cold front?

  d How do air pressure differences cause the wind to blow?

A web address you can explore is:

http://www.bbc.co.uk/weather/features/basics_airpressure.shtml

Using air pressure

You may have seen rubber suckers to attach toys to car windows or to hold hooks in the kitchen. If so, you have seen air pressure in use. When you press a sucker against a smooth surface, you squeeze out most of the air. Then, the sucker has low-pressure air inside it, and the high-pressure air outside it holds it in place.

Air pressure is also used inside bicycle and car tyres, to cushion bumps in the road.

When you use a drinking straw you are also using air pressure. Sucking on the straw lowers the air pressure inside the straw, and the air pressure pressing onto the drink then pushes it into the straw.

> **4** To do the magic card trick, you will need:
> - small glass
> - square of card 20 cm × 20 cm
> - water
> - sink or bowl
>
> This is what you do:
>
> **1** Carefully fill the glass up to the brim
>
> **2** Place the card over the top of the glass
>
> **3** Holding the card in place, turn the glass over. Do this over a sink or bowl!
>
> **4** Carefully take you hand away, leaving the card in place
>
> **5** Write down what happens

In the last activity, the card remains in place. You might imagine that the water would push it out of the way and spill into the sink or bowl. Instead, air pressure pushing on the card from below is enough to hold it in place.

You may have tried to pour liquid quickly from a drinks can. If you have, you will know that it is not easy. It would become easy if there was an extra hole, or if the can had a specially designed opening to let air in.

> **5** **a** Explain why it takes two holes in a can before it will pour properly.
>
> **b** Describe how you would remove a sucker from a wall. Explain what happens to the air pressure inside and outside the sucker.
>
> **c** Why does an old sucker, with damaged edges, not work as well as a new one?

Air pressure and tunnels

It can be very dangerous to dig a tunnel through very soft soil, or where water could seep into the tunnel. The sides of the tunnel could cave in, or the tunnel could flood with water before supports are put in place. To prevent this from happening, a technique called compressed air tunnelling can be used.

The air pressure inside the tunnel is increased by using compressed air. The additional air pressure helps to hold back loose material and water from the tunnel, and prevent it from collapsing. However, people working in compressed air conditions have an increased risk of 'compressed air illness'. Divers face similar problems, especially 'the bends'. Workers have to follow very strict safety rules when they use compressed air in this way.

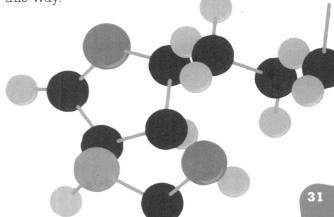

CAISSON

A structure is only as good as the foundations on which it rests. When the structure is a bridge or wharf, the laying of a secure foundation often requires a considerable amount of construction work on the floor of a body of water. In some cases, this can be achieved by building a cofferdam. Used since ancient times, this box-like structure holds back the water so that work can be done on the bottom. But in many instances a cofferdam is not sufficient, and a more elaborate structure known as a caisson has to be used.

There are many sizes, shapes and types of caisson. Caissons can be made out of many different materials; wood, concrete and steel have all been used successfully. Caissons come in three basic types: open, floating and pneumatic. The open caisson [a circular or rectangular tube], as the name implies, is open at both ends.

The end that rests on the bottom has a sharp edge. [Water is emptied by pumping air in.] As soil is removed, the caisson sinks under the force of its own weight. New sections may be stacked [at the top] as the structure sinks and settles onto bedrock. The caisson is then filled with concrete so that it can begin its service as a bridge pier, wharf foundation, or similar structure. A floating caisson is closed at one end so that it can be towed out to the site, where it is then sunk by filling it with sand, gravel, or concrete to serve the same purpose.

A pneumatic caisson is similar to the other types, but the top is closed so that compressed air can be pumped into its interior, preventing water and soil from entering through the bottom of the structure. The air pressure also offsets the pressure of the surrounding water, thereby allowing excavations to take place at depths of up to 40 m (131 ft). At this depth, a pressure of 360 kilopascals (52 lb per square inch) must be maintained [3.5 times atmospheric pressure]. The high pressure sets the limit of caisson depth, for anything higher cannot long be endured by most people.

The use of pneumatic caissons goes back to the middle of the nineteenth century, when Lewis Cubitt and John Wright used one while building a bridge in Rochester, England. Beginning in 1869, a pneumatic caisson was employed by James Buchanan Eads (1820–1887) when he directed the construction of the Mississippi River Bridge at St. Louis, Missouri. In the course of excavating a foundation for the bridge's piers, workers got down to 41.5 m (136 ft), still the record.

Of the 600 workers who worked in the caisson, 14 died from an ailment known as caisson disease or more graphically as 'the bends'. An additional 119 men endured the agony of this mysterious illness but survived. Caisson disease was caused because the high pressure increases the solubility of nitrogen in the blood, muscles and joints. When the worker returned to the surface, the nitrogen went out of solution and formed bubbles that caused excruciating pain and sometimes death.

Volti, Rudi. 'Caisson', The Facts On File Encyclopedia of Science, Technology, and Society. New York: Facts On File, Inc., 1999. Science Online. www.factsonfile.com

6 Read the article on the previous page about construction under water, and discuss the questions with a partner.

   a What is a cofferdam?

   b Why is it sometimes necessary to use a caisson?

   c Why is compressed air pumped into a pneumatic caisson?

   d What is the maximum pressure used? Why?

   e Describe why so many workers died in the early years of using caissons.

Review

Write each of the following questions onto a small piece of card. Shuffle the cards and then share out one question to each group in the class. Each group has five minutes to prepare an answer. In turn, the groups read out their question and give their answer.

- What is the atmosphere, and why do climbers become breathless at high altitudes?
- How can you demonstrate that air has weight?
- What did the Magdeburg hemispheres experiment prove?
- What is a barometer, and how can it be used to help us to predict the weather?
- Describe two ways that we use air pressure.

Chapter summary

In this chapter you have found out that:

- The particles of gas in the air move rapidly and collide with objects. These movements and collisions cause atmospheric (air) pressure.
- The pressure that results from the air in the atmosphere is approximately the same as 10 cars pressing down on each square metre.
- Air pressure varies from place to place, and becomes lower with increasing height above sea level.
- There are many uses of air pressure, such as drinking straws, suction devices and tyres.

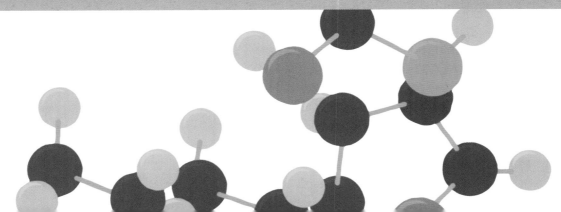

Spreading out

Introduction

In this chapter we look at how gases spread out, and what happens to solids when they dissolve in liquids.

- Gas particles are in rapid and random motion all the time.
- Gases mix by diffusion. In diffusion, gas particles move from an area of high concentration to an area of low concentration.
- Smells spread in this way.
- Some solids will dissolve in liquids to produce solutions, and others will not.
- When a solid dissolves in a liquid, its mass is conserved.
- A number of factors affect how much of a solid will dissolve in a liquid. These factors include temperature, stirring and particle size.

Make a list of your favourite food smells. Compare your list with that of a partner, and then work together to answer the questions.

- Why do you think we can smell coffee but not salt?
- Which animal do you think has the best sense of smell?
- Some people do not have a sense of smell. How could this be dangerous?

I n 1827 Robert Brown, a British scientist, was looking down a microscope at pollen grains suspended in water. He noticed that the grains were zigzagging backwards and forwards very rapidly. Pollen grains cannot propel themselves, so their movements must have had some other cause, but it was unknown at the time. This motion came to be called Brownian motion, after the man who first noticed it.

It was 50 years before Brownian motion was explained. A suspended particle, such as pollen in water or a smoke particle in air, is constantly battered from all sides by other particles. Pollen and smoke particles are so small that the even smaller particles hitting them cause them to move in the jerky pattern seen in Brownian motion.

This motion is very good evidence for the kinetic theory, which states that solids, liquids and gases are made up of tiny particles and that these particles are always on the move.

1 Work with a partner on the questions. When you have finished, compare your answers with another group.

  a Describe the differences between the arrangement of particles in a solid and a liquid.

  b Which of the following would show more Brownian motion?
   - pollen in water
   - smoke in air

  Explain your answer.

  c How does Brownian motion provide evidence for the kinetic theory?

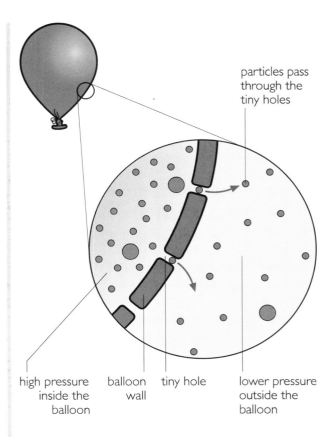

particles pass through the tiny holes

high pressure inside the balloon   balloon wall   tiny hole   lower pressure outside the balloon

Diffusion

If a small amount of bromine liquid is placed in the bottom of a gas jar, the liquid slowly turns into a gas or vapour. The bromine vapour slowly spreads to fill the container. This is because the bromine molecules are moving at random through the air. Eventually the bromine molecules are evenly mixed with the air everywhere in the jar. This spreading of a gas through the air is called diffusion.

Diffusion also occurs in liquids. If a small amount of dye is added to water, eventually it will spread out until all the water is evenly coloured.

A balloon lets itself down

You probably know what happens to an inflated balloon if it is left long enough. The balloon deflates and looks very wrinkled. The air has escaped from the balloon. This is because the molecules in air are so small that they can pass through tiny holes in the rubber of the balloon. The air, which is under pressure, diffuses out of the balloon. The air particles move from a region of high pressure where particles are close together to a region of lower pressure where particles are further apart.

2 Do other substances diffuse through a balloon?

To find out, you will need: *Wear safety goggles*
  - safety goggles
  - 8 balloons – not blown up
  - 8 droppers
  - 8 plastic cups
  - samples of vinegar, milk, coffee, sugar solution, lemon juice, perfume, vanilla essence

This is what you do:

1 Add two drops of one of the liquids to a balloon

2 Blow up the balloon and tie it

3 Place the balloon onto a plastic cup

4 Leave the balloon for ten minutes

5 During the ten minutes, set up other balloons to test the remaining substances

6 After each balloon has been left for ten minutes, smell the cup

7 Record which scent passed into the cup

8 Write down which substances diffused through the balloons

Animals appreciate fragrances

Female cheetahs at a New York zoo are great fans of Calvin Klein. Not the clothes he designs, but his perfumes. They don't dab a bit behind each ear, but they do rub against it on trees.

The perfume is sprayed on to the trees as part of a programme run by members of the Wildlife Conservation Society, the group that runs the zoos in New York. Apparently, giving the cheetahs different scents to explore stimulates them and keeps them interested in their surroundings.

Scents are very important to many animals, not least cheetahs. In case you are interested, the favourite aroma of cheetahs is Obsession for Men! Pity the poor pumas at the zoo – they prefer skunk urine extract!

Smells, show business and fear

Have you ever heard someone say that a certain smell reminds them of an important event in their life? You may even have said it yourself.

The sense of smell can trigger emotional reactions. For example, smelling a certain perfume can remind us of a particular person, place, holiday or other memory and make us happy or sad. Show business uses this fact, and smells can be used to add to the entertainment value of a show, film or even a CD.

Some performers have had their own 'scent' developed and this is released during a performance. There are perfumed inserts in some CDs, that will remind the listener of the performer and enhance the experience as they listen.

There is even a smell of fear. Animals such as dogs and horses can smell 'fear', and research has shown that some women can also do this. A group of women were presented with a mixture of armpit swabs from people who have watched a scary film, and from others who had not. The women could pick the ones that had the smell of fear. Men were not so good at this.

3 Many insects, including fruit moths, are guided to their mates by special chemicals sent out by the opposite sex. These chemicals are called pheromones, and many animals use them to attract mates. Work with a partner to complete the following activities.

a How do moths and other insects use diffusion to attract mates?

b Use the internet or books to find out more about how animals use smell.

c Prepare a small poster that shows how and why diffusion is vital to the animal world.

Dissolving

When you shake salt (sodium chloride) with water, the salt seems to disappear. The particles in the salt have spread out into the water and are now far too small to see. This is called dissolving. The salt still exists and there is just as much of it – as you add it, the volume of the mixture increases. We say that the mass of the salt is conserved.

4 Answer the following questions, and then compare your answers with a partner.

 a What is a solute?

 b What is a solvent?

 c Write down three examples of solutions.

Not all substances dissolve in water. Those that do are soluble. Those that don't are insoluble.

Liquids other than water are also solvents. For example, white spirit is used to clean (dissolve off) gloss paint from brushes, and nail varnish remover has a cocktail of solvents that dissolve nail varnish.

Solute	Solubility (g/100 g water at 20 °C)
sand	0
calcium carbonate	0.2
sodium carbonate	22
sodium chloride (salt)	36
sugar	211

Solubility of some common solutes as number of grams that dissolve in 100 grams of water at 20 °C

5 Work with a small group to investigate dissolving.

⚠ *Wear safety goggles*

You will need:
- safety goggles
- 5 test tubes with stoppers
- test tube rack
- water
- spatula
- samples of salt, sand, flour, coffee granules and sugar
- stopwatch

This is what you do:

1 Wear your safety goggles at all times

2 Half fill each test tube with water

3 Add one spatula measure of salt to the first tube and add the stopper

4 Shake the tube for 30 seconds and leave it to settle

5 Repeat this process so that you test each of the other four substances

6 After the tubes have settled, record your observations
- Of the substances you tested, which were soluble?
- Which were insoluble?

6 *Sc1* To get useful results, it is essential that we carry out fair tests. Think about the investigation you have just finished.

 a Which parts of the process helped you to carry out a fair test?

 b Which parts would you improve to make the test even fairer?

Increasing solubility

There are three ways to increase the speed with which a substance will dissolve and form a solution:

- heating
- stirring
- using smaller particle size for the solute

7 Work with a partner to plan an investigation to test one of the following hypotheses:

a A solute will dissolve faster in warm water than in cold water.

b 10 g of sugar grains will dissolve faster in water than 10 g of sugar cubes.

c Sugar will dissolve in stirred water faster than in unstirred water.

Include these points in your plan:

- Ways in which you would perform the investigation safely
- The equipment you would need
- A clear method describing exactly what you would do
- How you would make sure your investigation was fair
- How you would record your findings
- How you would use particle theory to explain your results

When you have finished planning, you will be asked to explain your plan to other groups.

Review

Work in a small group to carry out the tasks below. You will then be asked to explain one of your answers to the rest of the class.

Use the particle model and kinetic theory to explain these facts:

- Humans can smell perfumes and food from across a room.
- Insects attract mates using pheromones.
- An inflated balloon will eventually deflate.
- When salt is added to water it seems to disappear.
- Sugar grains will dissolve faster than sugar cubes.

Chapter summary

In this chapter you have found out that:

- In diffusion, particles move from an area of high concentration to an area of low concentration.
- Animals use the diffusion of scents to attract mates and to identify the source of food.
- A solution is made when a solute dissolves in a solvent.
- When a solid dissolves in a liquid its mass is conserved.
- It is possible to increase the solubility of a solute by heating the solvent, stirring the mixture or using a smaller particle size for the solute.

Making crystals

Introduction

In this chapter we look at how crystals are formed and review some of their uses.

- Saturated solutions are made in different ways.
- Most solids, including metals, are made up of small crystals.
- Gemstones such as diamond, ruby and sapphire are crystals.
- Rocks are made up of crystals of different sizes.
- Crystals have many important uses, such as in jewellery and liquid crystal displays.
- The crystalline substance known as common salt has been valued for thousands of years.

Work with a partner. Take two minutes to write down as many examples as you can of crystals and gemstones that you have seen and heard about. What are they used for?

 egend tells us that Ancient Greeks climbing near Mount Olympus were amazed to see a pure white material gleaming in caves. They called it krystallos, the Ancient Greek word for ice. The crystals were so attractive and hard wearing that they were traded much like precious metals such as gold and silver. The crystals were in fact the mineral quartz.

Quartz is only one of many different crystals that have formed in the Earth's crust. Many solids are made of crystals, but in most solids the crystals are too small to be seen with the naked eye. However, sometimes crystals can grow to be very large.

The legend of Amethyst

This is a story that has been told for four hundred years about one particular mineral, amethyst.

Bacchus, the god of wine, is in a very bad mood. He flies into a rage and orders that a beautiful woman should be thrown to the tigers. That woman is called Amethyst. However, before the tigers can attack Amethyst and eat her, the goddess Diana turns her into a hard white stone. Bacchus calms down and as an offering to the goddess Diana he pours wine over Amethyst, and the stone turns purple.

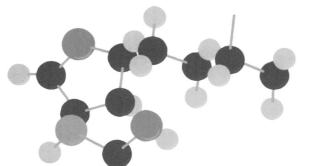

The magnified surface of the metal tungsten shows its crystalline structure.

A crystal is a solid with a regular shape. This is because its particles are arranged in a very organised pattern. The edges of crystals are straight and their surfaces are flat.

- Solids that are composed of crystals are called crystalline.
- Each crystalline solid has its own pattern.
- Solids without a regular shape are called amorphous.

The process of forming crystals is called crystallisation. This can happen in a number of ways.

- When molten solids, such as molten rock, cool, crystals start to form.
- In the lab, if a small crystal is added to a saturated solution, then this acts as the starting point for a larger crystal to grow.

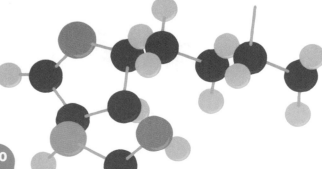

Saturated solutions

If you add salt to water it will dissolve. The salt particles spread out into the water. If you keep adding salt to the water, eventually no more will dissolve. There is no more room for the salt particles. A saturated solution has been formed.

The Dead Sea is a good example of a saturated solution. A lot of salt has been washed into the water, the hot Sun has evaporated much of the water, and the salt has formed crystals.

1 Work with a small group to grow some crystals of your own.

You will need:
- safety goggles
- glass beaker
- sugar
- small stick
- thread
- paper clip
- hot water (care)
- glass stirring rod

⚠️ Wear safety goggles

This is what you do:

1 Add the hot water to the glass beaker

2 Slowly add sugar to the water and stir

3 Keep adding the sugar until no more will dissolve

4 Give the sugar solution a final stir

5 Tie the paper clip to the stick using the thread

6 Place the stick across the jar so that the paper clip is hanging in the sugar solution

7 Make sure the paper clip is not touching the beaker

8 Cover the beaker and leave it to one side

9 Carefully observe the jar every few hours for a couple of days

10 Write down your findings and then try to explain what is happening to the sugar solution. Prepare to explain your ideas to others

Gemstones and crystals

We have many uses for crystals, and these uses are based on their properties.

Quartz

Quartz is a very hard, transparent substance that will even scratch steel. For this reason it is used to make a type of glass called quartz glass that is very hard wearing and also allows ultraviolet light to pass through.

When an electric current is passed through quartz crystals, they vibrate at a constant rate. This property is used to maintain accurate time in digital watches and clocks.

In liquid crystal displays, liquid crystal materials are sandwiched by quartz glass. We see numbers and letters on our calculators and watches because, when electricity passes across these particular areas of the quartz glass, it compresses the liquid crystals and they become opaque.

The following are some of the uses of quartz based on these properties:

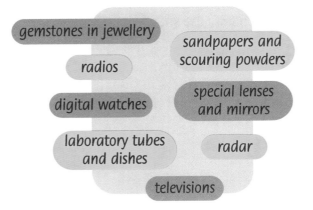

gemstones in jewellery

radios

sandpapers and scouring powders

digital watches

special lenses and mirrors

laboratory tubes and dishes

radar

televisions

2 Work with a partner to answer the following questions.

a Which properties of quartz make it useful in sandpaper?

b Which properties of quartz make it useful for jewellery?

c Quartz is a major component in the rocks sandstone and granite. Why are these rocks so hard and resistant to weathering?

The hardest substance known?

Diamond is famous for its hardness. It is almost impossible to scratch diamond, unless you use another diamond!

In 1833 Friedreich Mohs, an Austrian scientist, invented a scale for comparing the hardness of minerals. This is known as the Mohs scale for obvious reasons. It consists of ten minerals ranked in order of hardness. Minerals with a higher number can be used to scratch minerals with a lower number. The order of hardness in the Mohs scale is given below.

Hardness	Mineral
1	talc
2	gypsum
3	calcite
4	fluorite
5	apatite
6	orthoclase
7	quartz
8	topaz
9	corundum (colourless sapphire)
10	diamond

The steps between the hardness of the minerals are by no means equal – corundum is a little harder than topaz, while diamond is many times harder than corundum. It is only when we work out how to measure the hardness of the minerals that we see just how hard diamond really is. The Knoop scale is based on measuring the indentations made in minerals using diamond itself.

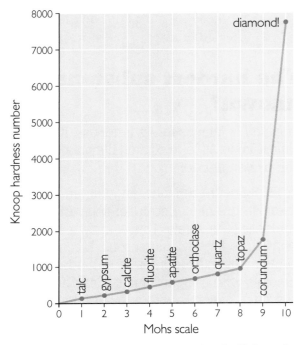

The **Knoop scale of hardness compared to the Mohs scale.**

Uses of diamond

It may surprise you to know that only 20 per cent of the diamonds dug from mines are used in jewellery. These are the clear, 'flawless' diamonds which can be sold for the best price.

The other 80 per cent of mined diamonds are flawed and so are not attractive enough to be used as jewels. But they are just as hard, and therefore find uses in industry. Industrial diamonds can also be manufactured: they are made in huge numbers by exposing carbon to very high temperatures and pressures. These conditions mimic the way that diamonds were formed naturally deep underground.

Worldwide, about 100 metric tonnes of industrial diamonds are used every year, mainly for cutting, grinding, shaping and polishing other hard substances. For example, diamonds are embedded into tools or turned into a paste to cut, polish and shape stones, ceramics, metals and concrete. They are used on the surfaces of very hard drill bits and tiny saws for precise surgical use.

Diamonds have other uses, too. They can be made into very special hardened windows, and tough surfaces for watches and for the tips of gramophone needles.

3 Answer the following questions and then write a short story or poem that uses the hardness of diamond as its main theme.

a Why is talc and not quartz used in talcum powder?

b Why are topaz, sapphire and diamond used as gemstones, whereas gypsum is not?

c Would quartz scratch fluorite? Explain your answer.

4 Work in a small group to design a poster that shows the properties of diamond and some of the uses of this very hard substance.

Ancient historical importance of salt crystals

In the past, salt was highly valued. In Roman times it was even used as money, and sometimes Roman soldiers were paid in salt. The word salary comes from the Latin word for salt. To look at why salt was and is so important we need to consider its uses.

From early times up to the present, it has been used for:

- flavouring food
- preserving food
- curing hides to make leather clothes and goods
- feeding cattle and sheep to make sure they obtain enough sodium and chloride

More recent applications include:

- spreading on roads to stop them icing up
- softening water to stop chemicals building up in kettles and boilers
- making sodium hydroxide
- making sodium carbonate, used to make glass and detergents

A strange use of salt is in removing tattoos! The process is called salabrasion. The salt is rubbed over the tattoo and up to 50 per cent of the coloured pigment can be removed. However, salabrasion can cause scars and is not a technique that should be used without expert guidance.

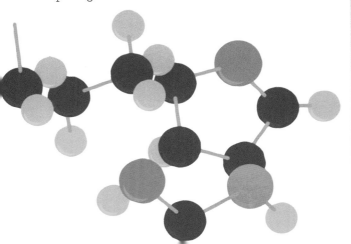

Purifying salt

5 Rock salt is a natural form of salt that can be dug out of the ground. It is a mixture of salt and a mud-like material called marl. To purify the salt you can try the following technique. Work with a partner.

You will need:

⚠ *Wear safety goggles*

- safety goggles
- rock salt
- pestle and mortar
- small glass beaker
- filter funnel
- filter paper
- spatula
- water
- evaporating basin
- stirring rod

This is what you do:

rock salt

pestle and mortar

add to water in a beaker

stir

filter the mixture

leave the liquid to evaporate

1 Wear safety goggles throughout the activity

2 Use the spatula to add a small amount of rock salt to the pestle

3 Use the mortar to grind up the rock salt into a fine powder

4 Add the powder to the beaker and add 100 cm³ of water

5 Stir the mixture for 2 minutes

6 Put the folded filter paper in the filter funnel and hold it over the evaporating basin

7 Pour the rock salt and water mixture into the filter funnel

8 Collect the liquid that passes through the filter paper (the filtrate)

9 Leave the evaporating basin to one side until the liquid evaporates

- What is left in the filter paper?
- What remains once the filtrate has evaporated?
- Discuss your findings and then produce a small poster that explains how purer salt is obtained from rock salt.

Review

Work in a small group to answer the following questions. Write down your answers and prepare to read them out to the rest of the class when asked.

- What is a saturated solution?
- Describe two ways that crystals can form.
- What is the hardest known substance?
- List two uses of quartz.
- Write down two ways that salt has been used for thousands of years.

Chapter summary

In this chapter you have found out that:

- Many solids are made up of small crystals.
- Diamond is the hardest substance known and is used to cut and polish other hard substances.
- Crystals are used in jewellery and liquid crystal displays.
- Crystals can form from the cooling of molten materials or from solutions.
- Salt has been so valuable in history that it has been used instead of money.

Introduction

In this chapter we look at how substances move through cell membranes and other barriers.

- Particles exist in different sizes.
- Smaller particles pass through barriers more easily than larger particles.
- Particles will move from where they are in high concentration to areas of lower concentration.
- Some particles will not pass through cell membranes.
- People with kidney disease use artificial membranes to clean their blood.

Take two minutes to write down some examples of filters that you have seen or used. Select one and draw a diagram to show how it works.

ilters and sieves have many everyday uses. A tea bag is an example of a filter you will be familiar with. The tea leaves are dried and chopped–up leaves of the tea tree. The bag enclosing them has many tiny holes that hot water can pass through. The leaves do not dissolve, but chemicals that are flavours and pigments dissolve out of them and mix with the water, forming the solution we call tea. The tea then passes out of the bag and into the cup or pot. The tea leaves are too large to pass through the tiny holes of the bag and so are not mixed with the tea.

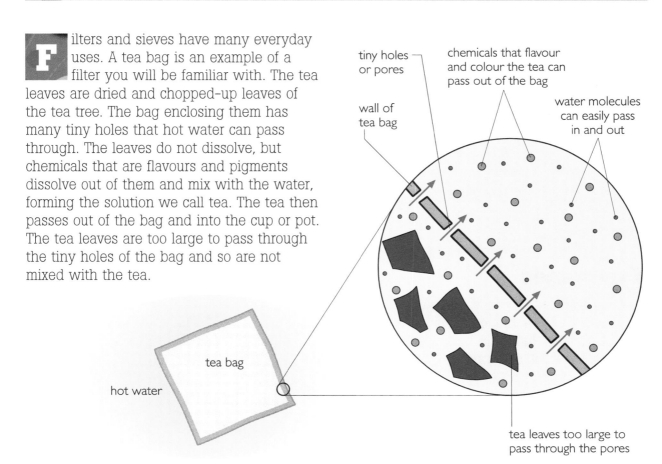

tiny holes or pores

chemicals that flavour and colour the tea can pass out of the bag

water molecules can easily pass in and out

wall of tea bag

tea bag

hot water

tea leaves too large to pass through the pores

1 Work with a partner to carry out the following experiment. You are going to use a sieve to try to separate sand and dried peas from water.

You will need:

Wear safety goggles

- safety goggles
- sieve
- two 250 cm³ beakers
- sand
- dried peas
- water
- stirring rod
- 100 cm³ measuring cylinder

This is what you do:

1 Add a small amount of sand and dried peas to one of the beakers

2 Use the measuring cylinder to measure out 100 cm³ of water

3 Pour the water into the beaker and stir the mixture

4 Hold the sieve above the second beaker

5 Carefully pour the sand, peas and water mixture into the sieve

6 Observe what happens

7 Write down your observations

8 Draw a labelled diagram of the apparatus

9 Explain your findings

Membranes

The outer surface of a cell is called the membrane. This membrane allows some materials to pass through it but not others. In this way, the cell can control what passes into the cell and what leaves.

Small particles such as gases, water and glucose can pass through the membrane easily. Larger particles such as starch cannot pass through.

Restoring water in cholera victims

A disease such as cholera can kill people, especially children, by making them lose too much water. If the people suffering from cholera are given large amounts of water with salt and sugar added, then they are likely to recover. The problem is that in many countries it is difficult to obtain water that is clean enough to drink. In fact, the water may have been the source of the cholera in the first place.

Water bags can be the answer. These are bags containing dry sugar and salt. When such a bag is put into dirty water, only the water particles can pass through into the bag. It acts as a membrane. The larger particles such as dirt and bacteria do not pass through the membrane. The clean water mixes with the salt and sugar, and a safe mixture is ready to drink.

2 Work with a partner. Use a piece of potato to act as a model of a cell. A potato piece contains many thousands of cells, each having an outer membrane that restricts the movement of larger particles.

You will need:

Wear safety goggles

- safety goggles
- two 250 cm³ beakers
- tap water
- salt (sodium chloride)
- two pieces of potato of the same size (2 cm × 2 cm)
- top pan balance
- paper towels
- spatula

This is what you do:

1 Find the mass for each piece of potato and record the values

2 Add 100 cm³ of tap water to each beaker

3 Add 10 spatula measures of salt to one beaker and stir until it dissolves

4 Add a piece of potato to each beaker and leave for 24 hours

5 After 24 hours, remove the pieces of potato and gently blot them dry

6 Find the mass for each piece of potato and record the values

7 Discuss your findings with your partner

• What happened to the two pieces of potato?

From high concentration to low concentration

Water will pass through a membrane from an area of high concentration of water to an area of low concentration. With pure water, every cm³ is made up of nothing but water particles. The water is at a concentration of 100%. With salty water, each cm³ contains water particles and salt particles. The water is not at 100%.

In the beaker of tap water – at 100% water concentration – water molecules move into the potato cells since they contain water at a lower concentration; the potato gains mass. The salty water in the second beaker is at a lower concentration than water in the potato, so water moves from a higher concentration in the potato to the lower concentration in the salt solution; the potato loses water and therefore mass.

Artificial membranes

Salty water can be a big problem for farmers in Australia. The salt can kill crops and the water is not suitable for drinking. However, there is very little alternative, since water is very scarce. This is frustrating because there are large amounts of salty water available, including unlimited amounts of seawater.

The Broken Hill Company may have solved the problem. The company has been working on a process that forces salty water through synthetic membranes. The membranes filter out contaminants in the water, including salt, bacteria, metals and even viruses. The membranes are so effective in sieving particles that they almost filter out particles from the water at the atomic level (see the next chapter: The atomic model after Dalton).

The company can filter in this way on a large scale. Typically, equipment that they supply will produce six million litres of water over the dry season.

The company is also looking to scale down the process. They hope that units can be made small enough to fit on boats. Surrounded by seawater, the crew would never be thirsty. However, they would need a powerful engine to work the pumps that force the water through the filters.

Artificial kidneys

The kidneys remove waste products and excess water from the blood. When kidneys stop working, the waste products build up in

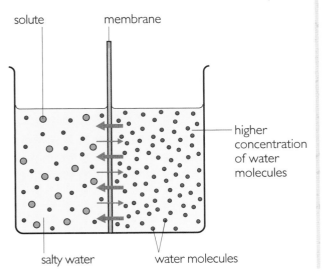

solute   membrane

higher concentration of water molecules

salty water   water molecules

the blood, and this is life threatening. Dialysis is an artificial way to remove these waste products. For this reason, a dialysis machine used by a kidney patient is often called an artificial kidney.

During dialysis, the blood passes through a special membrane made of a type of cellophane. This membrane contains many millions of small holes. The waste products pass through but the blood cells do not. The purified blood then passes back into the body.

3 Work with a partner to carry out the research activities. Make accurate notes of your findings and record at least two useful websites you used. At the end, you will need to plan and produce a leaflet explaining your answers and ideas.

- How do your kidneys act as a filter?
- What is dialysis?
- How are artificial membranes used to help people suffering from kidney disease?

A website you can explore is:
http://health.howstuffworks.com/question17.htm

Oil spill disasters

Spills of oil and fuels are a disaster for living things in and near the spill area. The oil and fuels contain many harmful chemicals and stick to rocks, plants and animals. The problem is especially severe in very cold regions of the Earth such as the Antarctic. Here, the temperature is so cold that the oil and fuels do not break down naturally as they might in warmer areas. The following extract explains how a team is trying a new technique to deal with a spill of fuel.

Keeping Antarctic oil spills in check

One solution is containment of the spill using physical barriers. This is the planned technique for a spill near a powerhouse in the Antarctic. The team is trialling some barrier technology. The barriers have porous membranes that allow water to pass through while trapping the fuel particles. The fuel is trapped inside the membrane barrier and can be collected later.

From *News in Science* –
www.abc.net.au/science/news/stories/s531789.htm

4 Work in a group to exchange ideas. Discuss the information about using membranes to help prevent oil and fuel spills. Then work together to produce a short piece of creative writing that explains how the membranes work. This can be a poem, a play or a short story.

Include these words in your writing:
- membrane
- holes
- particles
- particle size

How salty is the cytoplasm of cells?

When we place cells in pure water the water moves into the cells and makes them gain weight. If we place cells in very salty water, then water leaves the cells and they lose weight. If we add cells to water that is just as salty as the cell contents then, in theory, there should be no gain or loss of water by the cells.

5 In a group, you are going to plan an investigation to find out how salty potato cell contents are.

Consider the following questions to help you prepare your plan:

1 How will you be able to measure whether the potato pieces have lost, gained or remained the same mass?

2 How will you test a range of salt concentrations?

3 How will you make your test fair and minimise errors?

4 How will you record your findings?

When you have finished planning, you will be asked to explain your plan to other groups.

Review

You will be given a piece of A3 paper.

- Split the paper into four equal sections by folding or drawing lines.
- Working with your group, think up four questions about particles moving through membranes.
- Write down your questions, one each at the top of each quarter of your paper. Then pass the paper on to a nearby group.
- Answer the questions you have been passed, and prepare to discuss your answers with the whole class.

Chapter summary

In this chapter you have found out that:

- Sieves and filters can be used to hold back particles that are too big to fit through the holes.
- Cell membranes act as very effective barriers and only allow certain chemicals through.
- Water particles move from where they are in high concentration to areas of lower concentration, and this is very important in cells.
- Artificial membranes have many uses including kidney dialysis, water purification and the control of oil spills.

The atomic model after Dalton

Introduction

In this chapter we look at the structure of atoms in more detail:

- The atom is the basic building block of matter.
- There are only a few different types of particles in atoms.
- Atoms are made up of smaller sub-atomic particles.
- Atomic energy is made by splitting atoms.

Work with a partner. Draw how the particles are arranged in solids, liquids and gases. How does this arrangement explain the properties of materials?

ll the substances around you, whether gases, liquids or solids, are made up of extremely small particles called atoms. The existence of atoms has been discussed for thousands of years, and in Chapter 1 you read about the importance of the Greek philosophers and others in developing particle theory.

The English scientist John Dalton (1766–1844) suggested that all of the chemical elements that make up the materials around us are composed of atoms. His idea was that each element has its own, unique type of atom. Gold is composed of gold atoms, silver from silver atoms, and so on for all of the elements. This became known as Dalton's 'Theory of Atomic Structure'.

Dalton's theory includes these statements:

- All matter is made up of tiny particles called atoms.
- *Atoms cannot be created, destroyed or divided.*
- All atoms of an element have the *same mass* and the same properties.
- Atoms of different elements have different masses and different properties.
- Compounds form when atoms combine in simple whole numbers.

(The points in italic type have since been proved not to be true.)

Atoms were thought to be solid spheres, and it was understood that they could not be split down any further. This is true in chemical reactions, but we now know that atoms are made up of even smaller sub-atomic particles.

1 Carry out research into Dalton's theory of atomic structure. Use the internet and prepare a short report to share with others. Print out any useful pages you find, and record especially useful websites. You can try this one:
http://www.chemheritage.org/ EducationalServices/webquest/dalton.htm

Sub-atomic particles

The first sub-atomic particle, discovered by J.J. Thomson in 1897, was the electron, a very important, negatively charged particle.

Thomson devised a model of the structure of the whole atom. He thought that the electrons were spread around between the other, positive parts of the atom. The electrons, he thought, were like the sponge in a plum pudding, and the positive parts were like the plums. Hence, his model became known as the plum pudding model.

In 1911, the British scientist Ernest Rutherford (1871–1937) made a major discovery. He and his co-workers were studying the structure of atoms. They were firing large positively charged particles, called alpha particles, at a thin sheet of gold foil. It was expected that the particles would go through the gold foil, and this is what happened – in most cases. However, there were a small number of unexpected results. The alpha particles were deflected, or even bounced back! This was as if a heavy stone was thrown at a sheet of tissue paper and bounced back.

Rutherford understood the importance of the discovery. Most alpha particles went straight through because the atoms consisted mostly of empty space, but the few that were repelled showed that each atom had a small, positively charged central area. The nucleus had been discovered. The diagram shows the atom model after Rutherford's discovery.

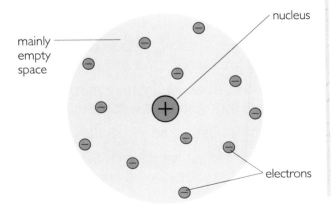

mainly empty space

nucleus

electrons

2 Work with a partner to research some of the key people who developed the idea of atomic structure. Select one of the following scientists and find out their contribution. Record when they lived, where they worked, a little about their background, and the ideas they had about atomic structure.

- J.J. Thomson
- Ernest Rutherford
- Neils Bohr
- Maria Goeppert

A modest man celebrated

Ernest Rutherford was awarded many prizes during his lifetime, including the Nobel Prize. He has appeared on stamps in Sweden, Canada, Russia and New Zealand (where he was born) and also on the New Zealand NZ$100 banknote. However, he is also remembered for his modesty and his desire to support other scientists in their work. He often did not put his name on important scientific papers, even if many of the ideas were his, in order to give credit to others.

The Bohr–Rutherford atomic model

Niels Bohr and Rutherford later agreed that in atoms there are three types of sub-atomic particles, and that they differ in mass and electrical charge.

Their properties are summarised in the table.

Particle	Relative mass	Electrical charge
electron	$\frac{1}{1838}$	−1
proton	1	+1
neutron	1	neutral

Our present understanding of atomic structure has not changed much since the atomic model that Neils Bohr and Ernest Rutherford proposed. In this model the electrons circulate round the nucleus in orbitals or shells. These are other aspects of the model we now use:

● The nucleus, which contains protons and neutrons, is the dense part of the atom.

● The number of protons gives the atomic number of the atom.

● Atoms have a balanced charge, so there are always the same number of electrons as protons in an atom.

● The number of protons and neutrons in an atom gives the atomic mass.

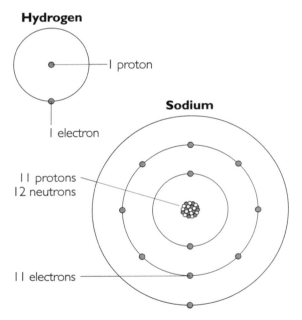

Atomic structure for hydrogen and sodium.

The first, innermost shell of an atom can hold up to 2 electrons. Hydrogen (see diagram above) has 1 electron in this first shell, and helium has 2 electrons. The second shell holds up to 8 electrons, and the third shell contains up to 18 electrons. Each shell must contain its maximum number of electrons before further electrons can occupy the next shell.

3 The atomic masses and atomic numbers are given below for four different types of atom. Use this information to help you complete the following activity.

For each type of atom shown below:

a write down how many electrons the atom contains

b write down how many protons the atom contains

c write down how many neutrons the atom contains

d draw the atomic structure.

● helium – atomic mass 4, atomic number 2

● carbon – atomic mass 12, atomic number 6

● oxygen – atomic mass 16, atomic number 8

● calcium – atomic mass 40, atomic number 20

Isotopes

It is possible for atoms of the same element to have different masses. This is because the number of neutrons in the nucleus varies. Such atoms are called isotopes. For example, hydrogen has these three different isotopes:

● Hydrogen has 1 proton, 1 electron and no neutrons: atomic mass = 1

● Deuterium has 1 proton, 1 electron and 1 neutron: atomic mass = 2

● Tritium has 1 proton, 1 electron and 2 neutrons: atomic mass = 3

We represent hydrogen by the symbol H. The isotopes of hydrogen can be written down as:

Hydrogen ^1_1H Deuterium ^2_1H Tritium ^3_1H

Tritium is not found naturally on Earth, but deuterium does exist in small amounts.

The extra neutrons in the nucleus can make some isotopes unstable. They can break up – they decay – and when this happens, the nucleus can give out radiation. This is radioactive decay. It is more likely to occur with very large, unstable atoms, such as uranium.

The energy released when atoms break up can be used in nuclear power plants, or can be used destructively in atomic or nuclear weapons.

The gradual breakdown of some isotopes can be very useful. One well-known use is in carbon dating. Living things contain carbon derived from carbon dioxide in the atmosphere. The carbon is a mixture of two isotopes, carbon-12 and carbon-14, each of known percentage in the atmosphere. Carbon-14 decays to carbon-12 in a living organism, but since it has a carbon turnover, the percentage of each isotope remains the same. Once the organism dies, the carbon-14 is not replenished.

By finding out how much carbon-14 is left, scientists can work out when ancient organisms once lived. The older the material, the less carbon-14 will be present.

4 Write down your answers to the questions below, and then discuss your answers with a partner.

   a Why do all of the isotopes of hydrogen have the same number of protons and electrons?

   b What is carbon dating and why is it useful?

   c Two isotopes of carbon are carbon-12 and carbon-14. The atomic number of carbon is 6. Work out how many protons, electrons and neutrons are present in each isotope.

   d Research one other use of radioactive decay.

New sub-atomic particles

Since electrons, protons and neutrons were discovered, over 200 much smaller sub-atomic particles have been identified. For example, it is now thought that protons and neutrons themselves are made up of smaller particles called quarks, held together by particles known as gluons.

To find out about atomic structure at this level, scientists use equipment called large particle accelerators (the accelerator, not the particle, is large). The accelerator uses huge electromagnets to speed particles round a long circuit and smash them at terrific speeds into atoms. The particles break up the atoms into smaller particles, and the tracks that these particles make are recorded and analysed by computers.

5 **a** Roughly how many sub-atomic particles have now been discovered?

   b What smaller particles make up protons and neutrons?

   c How do particle accelerators help us to understand atomic structure?

   d Look through comics, newspapers and magazines to find references to atoms and the atomic age. Are atoms described in a positive or a negative way?

6 For more about atoms, visit these websites:

   http://science.howstuffworks.com/atom.htm
   http://schoolscience.co.uk/content/5/physics/particles/index.html

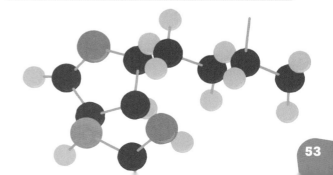

Review

📖 Work with a small group. On a large piece of poster paper, draw a timeline that shows how our understanding of atomic structure has developed since 1897. Put in the dates of major discoveries and the people who contributed to them.

Chapter summary

In this chapter you have found out that:

- Dalton's theory of atomic structure is still very useful, but atoms are now known to be composed of smaller particles.
- Ernest Rutherford was a leading scientist in forming our ideas about atomic structure.
- Atoms are made up of smaller sub-atomic particles called protons, neutrons and electrons.
- The number of protons gives the atomic number of an atom.
- The number of protons and neutrons gives the atomic mass of an atom.
- Isotopes of large atoms can be unstable and produce radiation.
- There are over 200 sub-atomic particles.

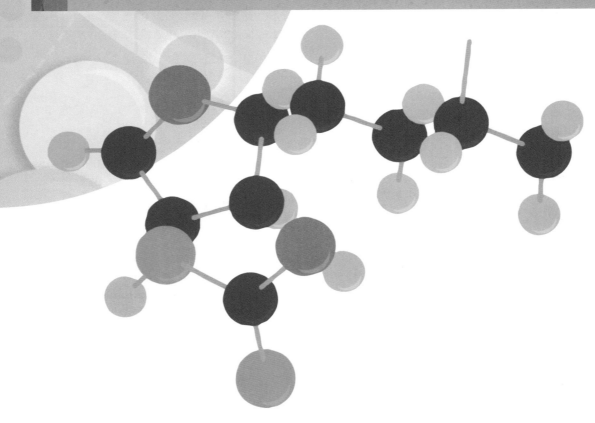

Elements, mixtures and compounds

Introduction

In this chapter we look at what elements, mixtures and compounds are made up of.

- Elements contain only one type of atom.
- Compounds contain different types of atoms chemically joined together.
- The elements in compounds cannot easily be separated.
- Elements and compounds can be represented by symbols and formulae.
- Mixtures contain two or more different substances that are not chemically joined together.

Make a list of five common mixtures. For each mixture, list the components. Discuss your list with a partner.

 s you know from Dalton's theory of atomic structure, elements are made up of only one type of atom. Aluminium is made up of only aluminium atoms, iron from iron atoms and so on. In all, there are 112 different elements, but some of these are very unstable and only exist for fractions of a second.

On Earth there are about 90 naturally occurring elements. All other substances are made up of various combinations of these elements.

Up until the eighteenth century, only about ten elements were known. Since then, elements have been extracted and purified from natural materials. In addition, 22 have been created which do not exist in nature.

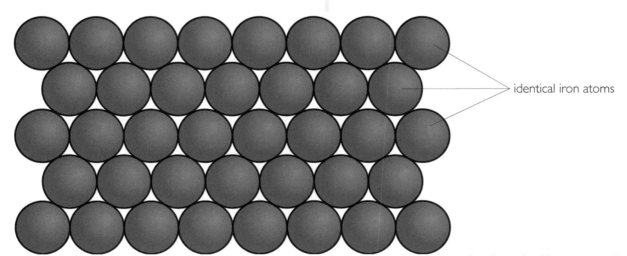

identical iron atoms

Iron is made of iron atoms only.

1 Work with a partner on this activity. You can use books and the internet, including the following website:

http://www.webelements.com/webelements/elements/text/Au/key.html

Gold was one of the very first elements known about and used. Research the physical and chemical properties of gold and explain why it was in use many thousands of years ago. You will need to find out:

- how easily gold reacts with other elements
- how it occurs in nature
- how easily it corrodes or wears away.

Early ideas about elements

The first elements used by ancient peoples were those that existed naturally. They were the elements that people found in their environment. Later, people developed chemical reactions that they could use to extract some elements from ores. These elements were mainly metals and were discovered in an order that is directly linked to how easily they were extracted.

This is the order:

1. Gold
2. Silver
3. Copper
4. Tin
5. Lead
6. Iron

Archaeologists have named periods in history after the metals used at the time, so we have the Copper Age, Bronze Age and Iron Age.

Copper tools have been found in Iran that date back to as early as 3800 BCE.

Bronze is an alloy (mixture) of copper and tin. The earliest bronze objects known were found in Mesopotamia, an ancient region in south-west Asia, and these date from 3000 to 2500 BCE. Bronze is harder than copper, and so was more useful for tools and weapons.

Extracting iron needs a much higher temperature than copper and tin. For this reason, iron making only appeared round about 1500 BCE. The iron was found in Asia Minor, the region now covering parts of Turkey. Africa became a major source of iron. In fact, the name of the country Malawi means 'land of flames', and it is thought that this refers to the iron furnaces that existed centuries before the industrial revolution in the UK. By 300 BCE, India was also a major producer of iron, and large columns were being cast with an expertise that did not exist in Europe for another two thousand years.

2 Work with a partner to answer these questions.

a Which was the first metal age in human history?

b When did bronze first appear?

c Why is bronze not found naturally?

d What is the meaning of the word 'malawi'?

The Ancient Greek 'elements'

The Ancient Greeks believed that substances were made up of a combination of four 'elements'. These were earth, water, fire and air.

Symbols

The modern elements all have names, but each can also be represented by a symbol. This is a very useful shorthand way of writing them down. These are the simple rules for writing the symbols of the elements:

- The symbol is often the first letter or the first two letters of the name.
- The symbol may be based on an older (usually Latin) name.
- No two elements can have the same symbol.
- The first letter is a capital letter, any second letter is a small letter.

Element	Symbol	Element	Symbol
Aluminium	Al	Magnesium	Mg
Bromine	Br	Nitrogen	N
Calcium	Ca	Oxygen	O
Carbon	C	Phosphorus	P
Chlorine	Cl	Potassium	K
Copper	Cu	Silicon	Si
Gold	Au	Silver	Ag
Hydrogen	H	Sodium	Na
Iodine	I	Sulphur	S
Iron	Fe	Tin	Sn
Lead	Pb	Zinc	Zn

The symbols for some common elements.

3 Work with a partner to answer the following questions.

   a Why is the symbol for helium not H?

   b What is the symbol for calcium?

   c Which element has the Latin name natrium?

   d Which element has the Latin name kalium?

The Romans, who spoke Latin, called lead plumbum. This is where Pb, the symbol for lead, comes from. Because water pipes used to be made from lead, this is also where we get our words plumber and plumbing.

4 For a visual interpretation of the elements, visit:

http://www.chemsoc.org/viselements/

Molecules and compounds

For some elements, single atoms do not exist naturally on their own but occur as pairs, since this is more stable. Examples are the gases in the air, oxygen and nitrogen. Each element exists as pairs of atoms joined together, forming molecules.

Compounds are substances made from different elements chemically joined together. In a compound, each identical group of atoms is a molecule, so a molecule is the single smallest part of that compound.

A very common compound is water. This is made from hydrogen and oxygen combined together. The water that is formed has very different properties from oxygen and hydrogen.

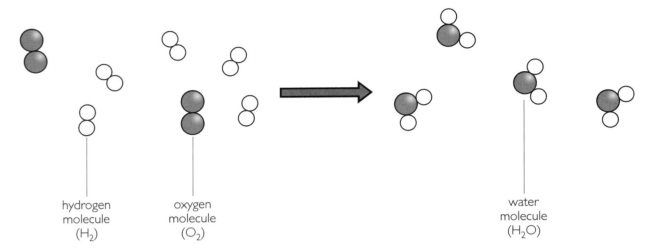

hydrogen
molecule
(H_2)

oxygen
molecule
(O_2)

water
molecule
(H_2O)

Water forming from hydrogen and oxygen.

5 Work with a partner. Review what you know about the substances below and then decide which are elements and which are compounds. Show your results as a chart and prepare to display your findings.

- Iron
- Iron oxide
- Sodium chloride
- Zinc
- Water

Mixtures

A mixture is a collection of different substances that are not chemically joined together. Some examples are shown below.

	Gas		
Gas	the air	**Liquid**	
Liquid	foam and sprays	emulsions such as hair oil; solutions such as beer	**Solid**
Solid	smoke	solutions such as salty water	alloys such as brass

Alloys are mixtures of different metals. Alloys are prepared because they have properties that are more useful than the separate metals alone. For example, adding chromium to steel helps it to resist rusting.

Amalgams

Amalgams are special alloys. We like them because we think mercury (Hg) is a pretty cool element. You might know mercury as 'quicksilver' or the metal that is liquid at room temperature. Anyway...

Amalgams are alloys that bring together mercury and other metals in the Periodic Table. The most obvious place you may have seen amalgams is in old dental work. The fillings in the mouths of your grandparents may have been amalgams.

We already talked about mercury being a liquid at room temperature. That physical property is used when they made fillings. Let's say you have an amalgam of mercury (Hg) and silver (Ag). When it is first created it is very soft. As time passes, the mercury leaves the amalgam and leaves the silver. The silver that is left is very hard. And voila... A filling.

From Chem4Kids.com:Matter:More Mixtures

6 Carry out a home survey.

- Ask your relatives and any other adults you live with about their early memories of visiting the dentist. Do they think they have had amalgam fillings?

- Check any metals you can safely see at home, and find out if any are alloys. Make a list.

- Write a brief report of your findings to share with others.

Separating mixtures

The components of a mixture are not chemically joined together. Usually this makes some of them easy to separate. The techniques for separating mixtures have been known for many centuries. For example, you can filter one component from another, rather like catching fish with a net – essentially a separation technique!

Two thousand years ago, a woman named Mary the Jewess was developing separation techniques and inventing laboratory equipment. Islamic chemists, such as Jabir ibn Hayyan in the eighth century, were experts at many chemical techniques and used distillation to improve the perfume industry. Al-Razi, one of Jabir ibn Hayyan's pupils, reported using many separation techniques and equipment that we would recognise today.

7 The separation technique we decide on for a mixture depends on the nature of the mixture.

Imagine that the mixture you are to be given is the result of an accident. A careless scientist was experimenting with different coloured inks and had mixed red, blue and black ink with water in a beaker. He then knocked some sand into the beaker. You will need to separate all these components from the mixture – the different dyes, pure water and dry sand!

This is what you do:

Sc1 1 Plan your investigation. You will need to decide which of the following techniques will be useful
  - distillation
  - chromatography
  - filtration
  - crystallisation
  - decanting

www 2 Research the techniques and select the most appropriate

3 Make a list of the apparatus you will need and show your plan to your teacher

4 Check the safety rules you will need to follow

5 Carry out the investigation

6 Report your findings to the rest of the class

Review

Work in a small group. Make a list of the different countries and cultures mentioned in the chapter, and then write down how each has contributed to our knowledge of elements and chemistry. Prepare to present your ideas to the class.

Chapter summary

In this chapter you have found out that:

- Each element has its own type of atoms, and elements can be represented by unique symbols.
- Ancient civilisations made use of elements, and the Greeks thought substances were made up of four – earth, water, fire and air.
- We now believe that there are about 90 naturally occurring elements.
- Compounds are made when elements combine.
- Techniques for separating mixtures can be traced back over many centuries and across many countries and cultures.

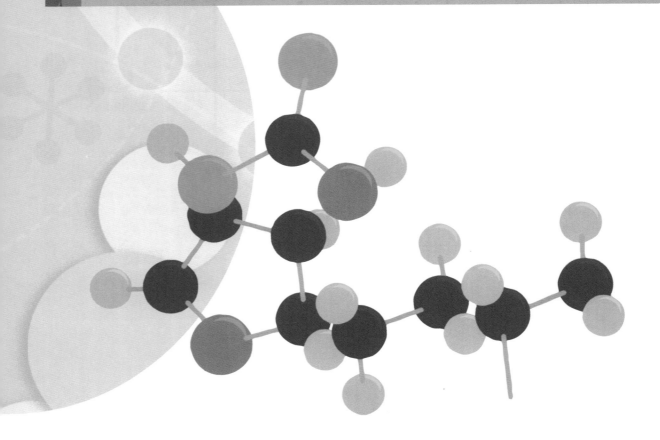

How atoms combine

Introduction

In this chapter we look at how atoms combine to make different chemicals:

- Atoms combine with each other in simple whole numbers
- Some atoms will react quickly together and others will not
- Atoms combine together through different types of bonding
- Some bonds are very strong and some are very weak.

Take a few minutes to write down the names of five compounds. List the elements that each one contains. Discuss with a partner how you think the elements actually hold on to each other.

Before we look at how atoms combine, we will need to think a bit more about their electronic structure. As seen on page 52, the electrons are arranged around the nucleus in shells. These shells contain a limited number of electrons before they are full.

Shells that are full are much more stable than shells that have spaces. When one atom combines with another, they both bond with each other in order to obtain a full outer shell. It is only the outer shell that is involved in bonding.

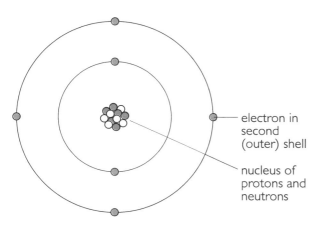

electron in second (outer) shell

nucleus of protons and neutrons

A carbon atom.

1 Draw the electronic structure of the following atoms. Show how many electrons are in each shell.
- Sodium
- Oxygen
- Neon

a Which is likely to be the most stable atom?

b Which is likely to be the most reactive element in the list? Give reasons for your answer.

Bonding

An atom can obtain a full outer shell in three different ways:

- giving up outer electrons
- gaining extra outer electrons
- sharing outer electrons.

Giving up electrons

If an atom has only a few outer electrons it can give these up. The loss of the electrons, which are negatively charged, leaves a positively charged atom called an ion.

A good example is sodium. Each sodium atom has just one electron in its outer shell. This is readily lost in reactions with other elements, and a positive sodium ion is formed. The ion is written as Na^+ to show that it has a single positive charge. A positive ion is called a cation.

Gaining electrons

If an atom is only short of a few outer electrons, it tries to gain some. Gaining electrons gives the atom a negative charge, and the charged atom is also called an ion. For example, chlorine atoms have seven outer electrons and need eight for a full shell. Once the extra electron has been obtained, the chloride ion is formed. This is written as Cl^- to show that it has a single negative charge. A negative ion is called an anion.

Look at the diagram. The positive sodium ion is strongly attracted to the chloride ion and when they react, a compound is formed called sodium chloride. This type of bonding in which ions are formed is called ionic bonding, and ionic bonds are very strong. The positive and negative charges attract in all directions, and the ions are held in a rigid structure.

Ionic compounds formed from positive and negative ions are usually solids, and they are difficult to melt or break down.

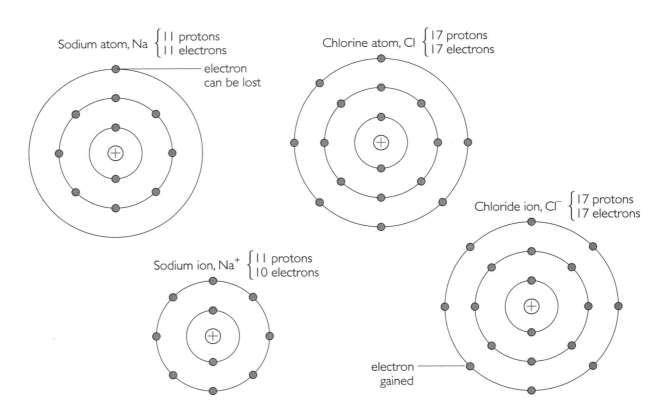

Sodium atom, Na $\begin{cases} 11 \text{ protons} \\ 11 \text{ electrons} \end{cases}$ — electron can be lost

Chlorine atom, Cl $\begin{cases} 17 \text{ protons} \\ 17 \text{ electrons} \end{cases}$

Sodium ion, Na^+ $\begin{cases} 11 \text{ protons} \\ 10 \text{ electrons} \end{cases}$

Chloride ion, Cl^- $\begin{cases} 17 \text{ protons} \\ 17 \text{ electrons} \end{cases}$

electron gained

2 Work with a partner. Look at the elements listed below. For each one:

a draw how the ions are made

b calculate its charge.

- magnesium atoms becoming magnesium ions
- lithium atoms becoming lithium ions
- fluorine atoms becoming fluoride ions
- oxygen atoms becoming oxygen ions

c Which of these ions will combine together to make ionic compounds?

d Write down the names of the compounds that would be formed.

Sharing electrons

Many atoms do not easily lose or gain outer electrons. An example is carbon, where the atom would have to either gain or lose four electrons. In such cases, the atoms share electrons. The electrons are shared in pairs between the atoms, and are called electron pairs. Where atoms are joined by shared electron pairs, the bonding is called covalent bonding.

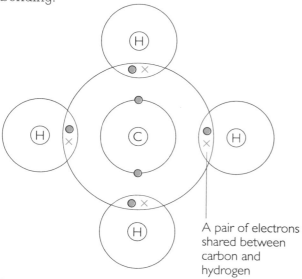

Bonding in methane, CH$_4$.

A pair of electrons shared between carbon and hydrogen

Covalent bonding forms molecules. The atoms in a molecule are held together strongly, but each individual molecule is only weakly held to other molecules around it. This means that it is easy to melt and boil covalent compounds, and at normal temperatures many are liquids or gases, as seen in the second table below.

Ionic compound	Melting point (°C)
potassium chloride	772
sodium chloride	801
silicon dioxide	1710
aluminium chloride	1902

Covalent compound	Melting point (°C)
water	0
chlorine	−35
ethanol	−117
methane	−182

3 You are going to investigate ionic compounds and covalent compounds. You will be given one sample of each. Carry out the tests and then write a report that shows the differences between covalent and ionic substances.

You will need:

- sodium chloride
- candle wax shavings
- safety goggles
- 4 test tubes
- 2 spatulas
- water
- Bunsen burner
- tripod, gauze and mat
- 250 cm³ glass beaker
- −10 to 110 °C thermometer

⚠ *Wear safety goggles*

This is what you do:

1 Look closely at the two compounds carefully – use the hand lens

2 Add a small amount of sodium chloride to water in a test tube. Stir it and record what you see

3 With a fresh test tube, repeat the test using the candle wax

4 Add a small amount of sodium chloride to a test tube and stand it in a glass beaker of water on a tripod, gauze and mat

5 Using a fresh test tube, do the same for the candle wax

6 Start heating the water with a Bunsen burner, and monitor the temperature

7 Observe the sodium chloride and wax for 5 minutes or until the water boils

Oxidation number

You may have used the memory aid OIL RIG to recall that oxidation is loss of electrons and reduction is gain of electrons. To consider loss and gain of electrons, let us look at the carbon shown in the methane diagram on page 63. It has formed four bonds, one with each of four hydrogen atoms.

Before reacting, the carbon atom had only 4 electrons in its outer shell, and now in methane it has 8. It has gained 4 electrons, each having a charge of −1. Though it is not an ion, we can think of the carbon atom as having increased its electrons by −4. We use this number 4 in the oxidation number of carbon.

For any element, the oxidation number shows the number of bonds that an atom of that element can form. If it gains electrons, its oxidation number is negative. So carbon has an oxidation number of −4. If an atom loses electrons, its oxidation number is positive. In methane, we consider that each of the 4 hydrogen atoms has 'lost' its electron to give carbon an outer shell of 8 electrons. We say that each hydrogen atom has an oxidation number of +1. Notice that when you add up the oxidation numbers for all the atoms in methane, the sum is zero, and this is the case for all compounds.

Knowing the oxidation number of an atom can help you to work out how it bonds and the kinds of compounds it will form.

Methane is a covalent compound. Now let us look at an example of an ionic compound – sodium chloride, common salt. Sodium has 1 outer electron which it readily loses, and so has an oxidation number of +1. Chlorine needs an electron to bring its outer shell to 8, so its oxidation number is −1. For this reason, sodium and chlorine bond together in a ratio of one to one.

Calcium has an oxidation number of +2. This means that in calcium chloride it would bond with chlorine in a ratio of one calcium atom to two chlorine atoms.

Positive ions			Negative ions		
Name	Symbol	Oxidation number	Name	Symbol	Oxidation number
sodium	Na^+	+1	chloride	Cl^-	−1
ammonium	NH_4^+	+1	hydroxide	OH^-	−1
copper	Cu^{2+}	+2	nitrate	NO_3^-	−1
magnesium	Mg^{2+}	+2	carbonate	CO_3^{2-}	−2
zinc	Zn^{2+}	+2	oxide	O^{2-}	−2
aluminium	Al^{3+}	+3	sulphate	SO_4^{2-}	−2

Oxidation numbers of ions.

Working out numbers of ions that react together

Ions may exist before a reaction, such as in solutions of compounds that are soluble in water. Alternatively, if elements (which have no charge) are involved in the reaction, ions may be formed as the reaction takes place.

Look at the table on page 64 showing the charges on ions. From the table, you can work out how many of one ion will react with another ion. (You have to imagine that elements have become ions.)

These are the rules to follow:

- Positive ions and negative ions combine together.
- Positive ions do not react with other positive ions, neither do negative ions react with other negative ions.
- Some elements can have more than one charge. So, for an element in the reaction you are considering, check that you have assumed the correct charge.
- In compounds, the charges are balanced – they cancel each other out.
- In a reaction, assume that only whole ions are involved.

Writing formulae

We can write compounds down as symbols in the same way we did with elements. The symbols for a compound make up its formula.

4 You are going to work out and write down the formulae for the following common compounds:
  A sodium carbonate
  B lithium oxide
  C magnesium chloride

For each one, this is what you do:

1 Write down the name of the compound carefully – some names are similar, so be careful.

2 Use a chart like the table on page 64 to look up the symbol and charge for the reacting substances. Assume that they are all ions.

3 Count the number of positive charges and the number of negative charges on the ions.

4 You will have to balance the positive and negative charges. If you have too many positive charges, you must add more of the negative ions. Similarly, if you have too many negative charges, you must add more of the positive ions.

5 Once the charges are balanced, you can write down the formula. Here is an example:

Name calcium chloride
Symbol Ca^{2+} Cl^-

There are more positive charges, so you must add extra chloride:

$$Ca^{2+} \quad Cl^-$$
$$Cl^-$$

Formula $CaCl_2$

The small $_2$ is used to show that there are two chlorides for every calcium.

6 Now you have a go with the compounds above.

7 Try to remember some of these formulae; they will come in useful!

Hydrogen bonds

Water molecules contain oxygen and hydrogen atoms bonded together, and the formula is H_2O.

The chemical structure of water is very similar to hydrogen sulphide, which is H_2S. The difference is that hydrogen sulphide contains sulphur and not oxygen. Hydrogen sulphide is a gas at room temperature, while water is a liquid. You might imagine that they should both be gases. The reason why water is a liquid at room temperature depends on a special form of weak bonding that occurs in H_2O but not in H_2S. This bonding is called hydrogen bonding and is shown in the diagram.

The hydrogen atoms in water have a slight positive charge. The oxygen atoms have a slight negative charge. Because of this, the hydrogen atoms are attracted to oxygen atoms in nearby water molecules. This helps to hold the molecules together and causes water to have a much higher boiling point than would otherwise be expected.

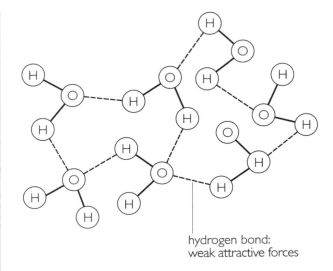

hydrogen bond: weak attractive forces

The mutual attraction between water molecules is also the reason that water appears to have a skin on the surface. Light objects such as small pieces of paper float on water, and some insects can walk across the surface of water.

5 Work with a partner. Research and then write a short presentation on the properties of water. Explain why:

a water has a high boiling point for a covalent compound

b water sticks to the sides of a glass

c insects can walk on top of water.

A web address you can explore is:
http://wwwga.usgs.gov/edu/mwater.html

Review

Work with a small group. Write down the name of a compound on a sheet of paper and then fold the paper. Pass it on to the next group. Once you have received another group's sheet of paper:

◯ write the compound down as a formula

◯ decide whether it is a covalent or an ionic compound

◯ describe one physical property you would expect the compound to show.

Chapter summary

In this chapter you have found out that:

◯ Atoms combine by giving up, obtaining or sharing electrons.

◯ The two main types of bonding are covalent and ionic.

◯ Covalent compounds are often gases or liquids, ionic compounds are often solids with high melting points.

◯ Compounds can be written in a short form called a chemical formula.

◯ Hydrogen bonding gives water some unusual properties.

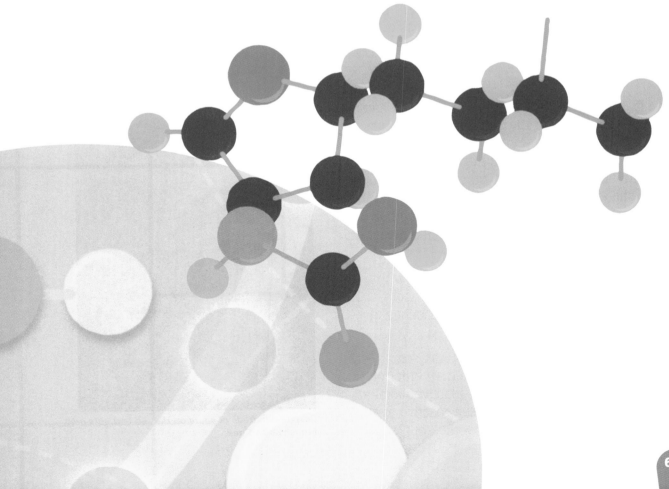

Atoms and patterns

Introduction

In this chapter we look at how atoms can be organised into a useful pattern called the Periodic Table.

- Metals react in a similar way with oxygen, water and acids, but some metals react more readily than others.
- We can use the differences in reactivity to create a reactivity series of metals.
- Elements are arranged in the Periodic Table in order of atomic number.
- The Periodic Table and reactivity series can help us to predict chemical reactions.

Take a piece of paper and write numbers 1, 2 and 3 down the left hand side.

- Next to number 1, write the name of a metal that is found as a pure element.
- Next to 2, write the name of a metal that is easily extracted from its ore.
- Next to 3, write down a very reactive metal that is never found as a pure element and is difficult to extract from its ore.

You have made a reactivity list of three metals.

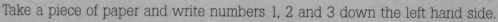

The gold brooch in the photograph had been under the sea since 1724. It was on the ship *Conde de Tolosa* when it sank near the Dominican Republic in the Caribbean. However, as you can see, the gold is still shiny. The ship that carried the gold was made of wood planking fixed together with iron nails. The nails have rusted away and disappeared.

Gold reacts with other chemicals only with the greatest difficulty. Iron reacts far more readily and undergoes chemical reactions in the seawater.

It is possible to arrange metals, and some other elements, into a list called an order of reactivity. We place the most reactive metal at the top of the list and the least reactive at the bottom. How is the list worked out?

Despite hundreds of years on the sea bed, this gold brooch still shines.

It is simple. The metals are tested to see how they react with air, water and acids. We say that the metals that react quickest are the most reactive metals.

When potassium is added to water, it reacts violently and the heat produced causes the hydrogen formed to burst into flames. Sodium reacts almost as violently.

Metals react even more violently with acids than with water. This is why we never add potassium or sodium to acids!

1 You can test some metals yourself, but not the very reactive ones.

This is what you need: ⚠ *Wear safety goggles*
- safety goggles
- dilute hydrochloric acid
- small pieces of zinc, copper, magnesium, iron, tin and lead
- 6 test tubes and a test tube rack
- dropper
- lighted spill

This is what you do:

1 Add a small amount of acid to each test tube and stand them in the rack

2 Carefully place a small piece of zinc into one of the tubes and observe what happens

3 Test any gas that is produced by lowering a lighted spill into the tube

4 Repeat the experiment using each of the other metals in turn

5 Draw up a league table showing the most reactive metal at the top and the least reactive metal at the bottom

- Which gas was produced?

Reactivity series

A more complete reactivity series is shown below. Two non-metals could be included: carbon between iron and zinc, and hydrogen between copper and lead.

- Metals that are less reactive than carbon can be extracted by heating their ores with coke, a form of carbon.
- Metals more reactive than hydrogen will react with acids and produce hydrogen gas.

Metal	Reaction when heated in air	Reaction with water	Reaction with dilute acid
Potassium	Burn vigorously to form oxides	React to give hydrogen gas and hydroxide	Violent reaction to give hydrogen gas and salt solution
Sodium			
Calcium	Burn but not as vigorously down the series	React with steam to give hydrogen gas and oxide	React to form hydrogen gas and salt solution
Magnesium			
Aluminium			
Zinc			
Iron			
Lead	React slowly to form a surface oxide layer	No reaction	No reaction
Copper			
Silver	No reaction		
Gold			

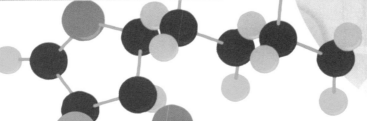

Potassium is more reactive than sodium or lithium, reacting vigorously with water.

His table was the result of a great deal of hard work. Firstly, he made a list of all of the known elements. Then he made a card for each one and wrote its name and atomic mass on the card. What Mendeleev did next was a brilliant piece of scientific work. He arranged the cards in the order of their atomic masses – he even left gaps where he thought undiscovered elements should fit. Years later, these gaps were filled by newly discovered elements, proving how clever Mendeleev had been to predict them.

Other scientists had already tried to assemble the elements into groups that had common reactions. However, Mendeleev's table was the best, and is the basis of the one we use today.

2 Work with a partner. Study the reactivity series and then answer the questions.

   a What is the most reactive metal in the series?

   b What is the least reactive metal in the series?

   c List three metals that will not react with acids.

   d List two metals that burn quickly in air to form an oxide.

   e Which metals react with steam to give off hydrogen?

Dmitri Mendeleev

Dmitri Mendeleev was born in Russia in 1834. He studied chemistry and became a school-teacher. He is famous worldwide for producing a table of the elements that arranged them into a pattern that, with a few changes, is used to the present day. He published this table in 1869.

3 Work with a partner. This is what you do:

   1 Collect 12 small pieces of card

   2 On each card, write the name of one of the elements below:

      hydrogen, helium, lithium, beryllium, boron, carbon, nitrogen, oxygen, flourine, neon, sodium, magnesium

   3 Look up the atomic mass and atomic number for each element and write them onto the card

   4 Onto each card, draw the electronic arrangement of the atoms

   5 Arrange the cards in an order that is based on the increasing size of the atoms
     • What pattern do you get?

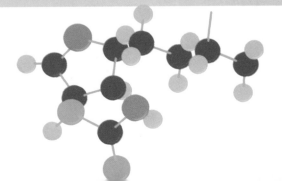

The Periodic Table

Key

	atomic mass
symbol	name
	atomic number

■ metals □ non-metals

The following table lists each element as *symbol (atomic mass, atomic number)*.

Group	I	II	transition metals →										III	IV	V	VI	VII	0
Period 1	H (1, 1)																	He (4, 2)
Period 2	Li (7, 3)	Be (9, 4)											B (11, 5)	C (12, 6)	N (14, 7)	O (16, 8)	F (19, 9)	Ne (20, 10)
Period 3	Na (23, 11)	Mg (24, 12)											Al (27, 13)	Si (28, 14)	P (31, 15)	S (32, 16)	Cl (35.5, 17)	Ar (40, 18)
Period 4	K (39, 19)	Ca (40, 20)	Sc (45, 21)	Ti (48, 22)	V (51, 23)	Cr (52, 24)	Mn (55, 25)	Fe (56, 26)	Co (59, 27)	Ni (59, 28)	Cu (64, 29)	Zn (65, 30)	Ga (70, 31)	Ge (73, 32)	As (75, 33)	Se (79, 34)	Br (80, 35)	Kr (84, 36)
Period 5	Rb (85.5, 37)	Sr (88, 38)	Y (89, 39)	Zr (91, 40)	Nb (93, 41)	Mo (96, 42)	Tc (99, 43)	Ru (101, 44)	Rh (103, 45)	Pd (106, 46)	Ag (108, 47)	Cd (112, 48)	In (115, 49)	Sn (119, 50)	Sb (122, 51)	Te (128, 52)	I (127, 53)	Xe (131, 54)
Period 6	Cs (133, 55)	Ba (137, 56)	La (139, 57)	Hf (178.5, 72)	Ta (181, 73)	W (184, 74)	Re (186, 75)	Os (190, 76)	Ir (192, 77)	Pt (195, 78)	Au (197, 79)	Hg (201, 80)	Tl (204, 81)	Pb (207, 82)	Bi (209, 83)	Po (210, 84)	At (210, 85)	Rn (222, 86)
Period 7	Fr (223, 87)	Ra (226, 88)	Ac (227, 89)	Db Dubnium (104)	Jl Joliotium (105)	Rf Rutherfordium (106)	Bh Bohrium (107)	Hn Hahnium (108)	Mt Meitnerium (109)									

Trend: metal → non-metal

The modern Periodic Table

The Periodic Table we use today is an arrangement of all the known elements in order of their atomic numbers. The position of an element in the Periodic Table helps us to understand its physical and chemical properties.

The table is divided into *groups* and *periods*.

A group is a vertical column of elements. These groups are given roman numbers, and several also have names. The elements in the same group have the same number of outer electrons, and because of this they react in very similar ways.

A period is a horizontal row of elements. There are seven periods. Moving from left to right across a period, the atomic number of each element increases by one. So each element has one more electron in the outer shell than the element to its left. The elements in a period all have the same number of shells, and so their chemical properties change gradually as we move from left to right.

Work with a partner. You are going to select one of the groups listed below and carry out research.

- The alkali metals
- The alkaline earth metals
- The halogens
- The noble gases

You may wish to use books or the internet. For the group you select, do the following:

1 Find out and record how reactive the elements are

2 Explain what happens to their reactivity as you move down the group

3 Find the names of some of the compounds the elements make, if any.

4 Record some of the uses of the elements and their compounds

The transition metals

Elements in the central block of the Periodic Table are known as the transition metals. Many of these metals are very well known and have many uses. Examples you have probably heard of include iron, copper, zinc, cobalt, nickel, silver, gold, mercury and platinum.

Iron

Iron is probably the most used transition metal. A poem by Roger McGough speaks for iron and how much we depend on it! This is an extract from his poem.

Iron

Fe fi fo fum
As hard as nails
As tough as they come

I'm the most important
Metal known to man
(though aluminium
is more common
do we need another can?)

Five percent of the Earth's crust
I am also the stone at its centre
Iron fist in iron glove
Adding weight to the system
I am the firma in the terra

Fe fi fo
Don't drop me on your toe

My hobbies are space travel
And changing the course of history
(they even named an age after me
– eat your heart out Gold)

From Defying Gravity by Roger McGough,
Penguin 1993.

5 a Read the poem about iron, and write in your own words what it is telling you about this important transition metal.

b Then select any other element from the Periodic Table and write your own poem. Try to convey to the reader why the element is useful.

Review

Work with a partner. Write down the words TRUE and FALSE on two separate pieces of card. When each of the following questions are read out, hold up one of the cards to give your answer.

- Maglev developed the Periodic Table we use today.
- Elements in the same group in the Periodic Table have similar chemical properties.
- Sodium and potassium react violently with water.
- Gold and silver are very reactive metals.
- Zinc will react with hydrochloric acid.
- Iron is a transition metal.

Chapter summary

In this chapter you have found out that:

- The metals can be put into a reactivity series with the most reactive metals at the top.
- All of the elements can be arranged into a table called the Periodic Table.
- The elements in the Periodic Table are arranged in order of atomic number.
- The table groups similar elements together and can be used to predict reactions.
- The transition metals are a special collection of elements that have many important uses.

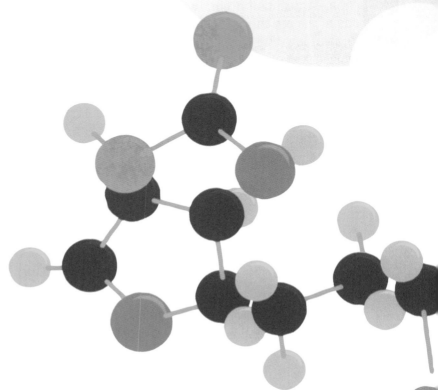

Particles and chemical reactions

Introduction

In this chapter we look at how chemical reactions can be written as equations using symbols:

- Chemical equations use simple symbols to show what happens in a chemical reaction.
- During a chemical reaction, matter is not created or destroyed.
- Chemical equations show exactly how many atoms take place in a reaction and what happens to them.
- Using chemical equations is a good example of using models in science.

Write down two examples of chemical reactions you have seen. For each reaction, list the chemicals that reacted (the reactants) and the chemicals that were made (the products). Compare your examples with those of a partner.

 chemical reaction occurs when chemicals are mixed together and react to give new chemicals. The atoms in the chemicals are rearranged into new patterns. This involves the breaking and making of bonds between the atoms.

- Breaking a chemical bond requires energy.
- Making a chemical bond releases energy.

Both of these events happen during every chemical reaction.

1 Work with a partner. For each of the reactions below, list the reactants and the products.

a When hydrochloric acid and calcium are mixed, they react to give hydrogen and calcium chloride.

b Copper sulphate and water can be produced by reacting copper oxide and sulphuric acid together.

c When sodium burns in oxygen, a white powder called sodium oxide is made.

Cooking is chemistry

You will find many more chemicals in your kitchen at home than you are likely to use in your science lessons. The important chemicals in food, such as proteins, fats and carbohydrates, are complicated chemicals, but they are still made up of very few different elements. These are mainly carbon, hydrogen, oxygen, nitrogen and sulphur – which you could remember as CHONS.

2 **a** Why are proteins and fats important in our food?

b Why must we eat carbohydrates as part of a healthy diet?

Many foods can be eaten uncooked. However, cooking food can improve flavours and kills some of the bacteria that could be harmful. Cooking changes the way that food tastes because the heat of the cooking causes chemical reactions. This produces new chemicals. However, research seems to show that over-cooking food can be dangerous.

Is the barbecue dangerous?

3 To find out more about this question, read the extract from this website:

www.cbsnews.com/stories/2001/05/21/summer/main292536.shtml

Six Ways to Make Your Barbecues Healthier

One of the most popular rites of summer is the outdoor cookout. Unfortunately, evidence suggests that foods cooked on a charcoal, gas, or electric grill may be hazardous to your health.

The National Academy of Sciences has

4 Work with a partner. Use the extract below to help you to design a small warning poster to be fixed to the lids of barbecues. The poster should:

- explain the possible risks of grilling food
- reassure people that if they are sensible there is little health risk
- offer practical advice to prevent over-grilling or charring the food.

discovered a possible link between the grilling of food and the development of what are believed to be cancer-causing compounds. Some researchers suspect that when high-fat, high-protein foods, like hamburgers, are exposed to the intense, searing heat of barbecue cooking, the fat and protein turn into mutagens, chemicals that can damage the genetic material of cells and possibly cause cancer.

Since the jury is still out on whether or not grilled food definitely causes cancer, it's probably wise to reserve barbecuing for special occasions, rather than grill food regularly.

⚠ Before cooking meat or poultry (or fish, if applicable), trim away fat. And don't baste foods to be grilled with butter or oil.

⚠ Keep a spray water bottle handy to douse flare-ups.

⚠ Position food well above the heat source.

⚠ If noticeable amounts of fat drip and flare up as food cooks, lower the flame or move the food to another part of the grill.

⚠ Cook food until it's done, but avoid charring it. The longer food is grilled and the blacker it gets, the higher the risk.

⚠ To avoid charring fish and vegetables, wrap them in aluminum foil.

Chemical equations

Maybe you remember how we used symbols and formulae as a shorthand way of writing down the names of elements and compounds. We can also show whole chemical reactions in a similar way. The shorthand way of writing down a chemical reaction is called a chemical equation. This is an example:

In words:

When hydrochloric acid is added to calcium carbonate there is a chemical reaction. A gas, carbon dioxide, is produced. The other products are calcium chloride and water.

As an equation:

hydrochloric acid + calcium carbonate → calcium chloride + carbon dioxide + water

$$2HCl \quad + \quad CaCO_3 \quad \rightarrow \quad CaCl_2 \quad + \quad CO_2 \quad + \quad H_2O$$

Before we think about writing equations, let's look at how much information they give us.

- The 2 in front of the hydrochloric acid formula tells us that we need two molecules of acid for every calcium carbonate used.
- The small numbers show us how many atoms of each element are found in each compound.

Writing equations

Here are some rules for writing chemical equations:
- Write the equation down in words – check that this is correct before you go on.
- Find the symbol for each atom and the formula for each compound.
- Write the formulae and symbols underneath the word equation.
- Balance the equation by making sure that every atom on one side can be found on the other – remember that matter cannot be created or destroyed in a chemical reaction.

For example:

Word equation: zinc + hydrochloric acid → zinc chloride + hydrogen

Symbols: $Zn \ + \quad HCl \quad \rightarrow \quad ZnCl_2 \quad + \quad H_2$

To balance the equation we need to make sure that there are exactly the same number of atoms on both sides. There are two chlorides in the products, but the acid compound only adds one. Therefore we need to add extra acid. This also helps to balance the hydrogen, since hydrogen exists as two hydrogen atoms joined together in a molecule of the gas.

Balanced equation:

$$Zn + 2HCl \rightarrow ZnCl_2 + H_2$$

5 With a partner, work out the correct chemical equations for the following word equations.

a copper oxide + hydrochloric acid → copper chloride + water

b zinc + sulphuric acid → zinc sulphate + hydrogen

c calcium carbonate + hydrochloric acid → calcium chloride + carbon dioxide + water

Modelling in science

When we talk about modelling in science, we are not talking about making models of objects, such as planes or ships. The models we use in science are models in the mind. These models are descriptions of scientific facts or events, and were developed to help us understand things we cannot see. The models represent how we think the world works.

As an example of a scientific model, think of the way we represent atomic structure. We cannot actually see the sub–atomic particles, and it is very unlikely that atoms look exactly like the drawings in books. But these drawings are useful models because they represent atoms in a way that helps us to explain how atoms actually behave.

Chemical equations are also models. They describe materials and reactions in the real world. The chemicals themselves do not have symbols, small numbers or brackets! Reactions do not have plus signs or arrows. We draw the equation to explain what is taking place during a reaction – the reaction does not look like this.

The table below shows four ways that models are used in science.

6 Work with a partner.

- Think back to the science ideas you have studied so far this year.

- Make a list of the scientific models that have been used to help you to understand the ideas.

- For each model, try to decide which of the four categories in the table it would belong to.

Category of model	How it works	Examples
Physical models	These are smaller versions of the real thing so they can be touched and examined	Models of the Solar System Model rockets
Representations	These are objects that represent the real world but do not look exactly like it	Maps Drawings and diagrams
Analogy	Examples from the real world are used to explain the scientific idea	The flow of water being used to explain electricity Atomic structure being described as a mini Solar System
Theoretical	Unseen forces or object are invented to explain observations. Sometimes these are later discovered!	Atoms described by Greek philosophers Gravity described by Newton

Computer modelling

Computers are now used to build up models of many aspects of the world, so that we can better understand them. For example, computer modelling is used to forecast weather, investigate global warming, predict earthquakes and study chemical reactions.

Computer models can be used to predict what happens if conditions change. For example, we can take the computer model of a chemical reaction and alter the conditions in it, such as temperature or concentration. In this way, we can find out what will happen without actually doing the experiment!

The chemist is studying a computer model of a drug (thick structure) that has been designed to react with a cell enzyme (surrounding structure). This reaction is intended to prevent cancer cells from dividing.

Review

The class should be split into four teams. You have one minute to discuss each of the questions below and write down your answer. At the end, the correct answer will be given and teams score one point for each correct answer. The winning team is the one with the most points.

- When calcium reacts with hydrochloric acid, one product is hydrogen gas. What is the other?
- Balance this equation: $HCl + CaCO_3 \rightarrow CaCl_2 + H_2O + CO_2$
- Why must a chemical equation be balanced?
- Cooking involves chemical reactions. Why should we not eat charred food?
- Give one example of a model used to explain a scientific idea.

Chapter summary

In this chapter you have found out that:

- Chemical reactions can be written down in a shorthand way called an equation.
- Both sides of a chemical equation must have the same number of atoms.
- Cooking involves many chemical reactions.
- Overcooking food so that it chars can be harmful to health.
- Scientists use models to help them to explain the world around us.
- Computer models have many uses and allow scientists to test ideas quickly.

Particles and energy

Introduction

In this chapter we look at the energy changes that take place during chemical reactions:

- Reactions that give out heat are called exothermic.
- Burning a fuel is an example of an exothermic reaction.
- Some exothermic reactions are very violent and dangerous.

- Reactions that require heat are called endothermic reactions.
- We use many different sources of energy, including fossil fuels.
- Burning fossil fuels can cause environmental damage.

You will have used many different types of fuels to provide energy. Take two minutes to make a list of the fuels you have used, and for each one write down what the energy was used for.

Methane is an example of a fuel, and is probably the gas you use at home. When methane gas in the gas ring or gas fire burns, we notice some important changes. Methane is a transparent (clear) gas, and is impossible to see. It burns with a blue, hot flame, which shows that burning the gas gives us heat and light.

The burning of methane also forms chemical products. These are:

- water
- carbon dioxide

A chemical equation for the reaction is:

methane + oxygen → carbon dioxide + water

$$CH_4 + 2O_2 \rightarrow CO_2 + 2H_2O$$

1 Work with a partner on this activity.

- Write a short newspaper article that explains what would happen to us all if there were no fuels left on Earth.

- Before you start, make a list of the many purposes we use fuels for, and discuss the problems that would result if these things could no longer take place.

- Finally, highlight the one thing you would miss above all if the last of the fuel on Earth was used up yesterday!

How do we get energy from fuels?

Chemical reactions that give out heat are called exothermic reactions. During all chemical reactions, bonds are broken and new bonds are formed. To see how this can result in energy being given out, let us look at the burning of methane in more detail.

There is a lot of energy stored in molecules of methane and oxygen (the reactants). Molecules of water and carbon dioxide (the products) contain less energy. This means that when methane reacts with oxygen to give water and carbon dioxide, there is a surplus of energy available. The extra energy is released into the surroundings.

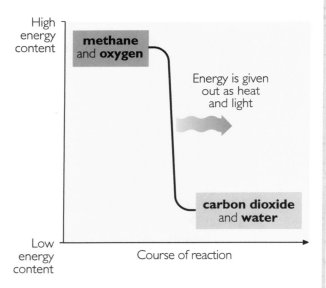

Energy diagram for the exothermic reaction of methane burning.

Not all fuels give out the same amount of energy. We compare fuels by working out how much energy, measured in kilojoules, we get from each gram of fuel.

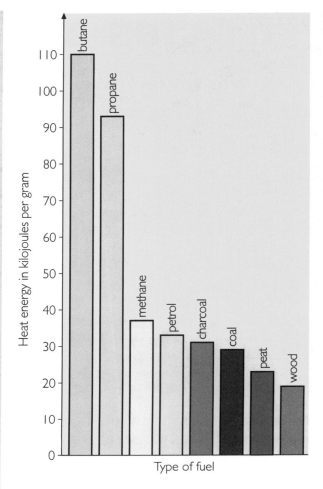

Heat energy from different fuels.

2 Work with a partner to carry out these tasks:

a Write down the name of the fuel that gives the most energy per gram.

b Write down the name of the fuel that gives the least energy per gram.

c When choosing a fuel, what other factors would you want to take into account?

d When petrol burns fully, it gives carbon dioxide and water. Draw an energy chart for petrol. Use the one for methane to give you some guidance.

Ignition!

Burning, or combustion, usually takes place in air. It is the oxygen in the air that actually supports the burning. However, we can leave fuels in air without them burning. This is because combustion needs to be started by heat. Applying heat to start a reaction is called ignition. The three ingredients needed before fuels will burn are often represented by a triangle, called the triangle of fire, as shown in the diagram.

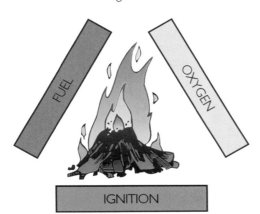

Sometimes exothermic reactions can be explosive and tragic. A children's song describes a very famous exothermic reaction on a grand scale!

London's burning, London's burning

Fetch the engine, Fetch the engine

Fire! Fire! – Fire! Fire!

Pour on water, Pour on water

One of the most famous fires in history – the Great Fire of London – started on 2 September 1666. That Sunday morning saw the start of a fire that would destroy most of London, as it was then. The scale of the fire was huge – buildings over an area of two square kilometres burned down. More than 1300 houses and 87 churches were lost.

Amazingly, very few people lost their lives. It is difficult to get an actual figure, but it could have been less than ten. Many people think that the fire helped to save lives, because in the previous year over 1700 people had been killed by the plague – a disease carried by rats. The fire killed countless rats, and also made room for a newer, cleaner more modern city to be built.

Samuel Pepys described the fire in the following extract from his famous diary.

So I made myself ready presently, and walked to the Tower; and there got up upon one of the high places, ... and there I did see the houses at the end of the bridge all on fire, and an infinite great fire on this and the other side ... of the bridge.

So down, with my heart full of trouble, to the Lieutenant of the Tower, who tells me that it began this morning in the King's baker's house in Pudding Lane, and that it hath burned St Magnus's Church and most part of Fish Street already. So I rode down to the waterside, ... and there saw a lamentable fire. ... Everybody endeavouring to remove their goods, and flinging into the river or bringing them into lighters that lay off; poor people staying in their houses as long as till the very fire touched them, and then running into boats, or clambering from one pair of stairs by the waterside to another. And among other things, the poor pigeons, I perceive, were loth to leave their houses, but hovered about the windows and balconies, till they some of them burned their wings and fell down.

Having stayed, and in an hour's time seen the fire rage every way, and nobody to my sight endeavouring to quench it, ... I to Whitehall (with a gentleman with me, *who desired to go off from the Tower to see the fire in my boat); and there up to the King's closet in the Chapel, where people came about me, and I did give them an account [that] dismayed them all, and the word was carried into the King. So I was called for, and did tell the King and Duke of York what I saw; and that unless His Majesty did command houses to be pulled down, nothing could stop the fire. They seemed much troubled, and the King commanded me to go to my Lord Mayor from him, and command him to spare no houses.*

3 Work with a partner. Answer the questions and then prepare a poster describing how fires such as the Great Fire of London are examples of exothermic reactions.

a How did the Great Fire of London start?

b What was the main fuel that burned?

c List two forms of energy that were produced by the fire.

d During the fire, buildings were pulled down ahead of the fire. Why?

e How did the fire ultimately save lives?

f How does pouring on water help to put out a fire?

Endothermic reactions

Reactions that require heat to keep them going are called endothermic reactions: the reacting materials contain less energy than the product materials, so the reactants require an input of heat energy to maintain the reaction. This input comes from the surroundings (for example, from a Bunsen burner), so the surroundings lose a certain amount of heat energy to the reactants in order to form the products. The amount of heat energy required equals the heat energies of the products minus the heat energies of the reactants.

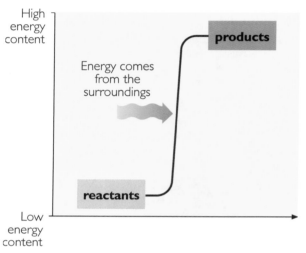

Energy diagram for endothermic reactions

When soluble substances, which are ionic, dissolve in water, there is a reaction. The bonds between the ions of the substance are broken, and the ions disperse separately in amongst the water molecules. An example of such a reaction is when ammonium nitrate (NH_4NO_3) is dissolved in water to form ammonium ions and nitrate ions. This is a very endothermic reaction – it requires a lot of energy. This energy is taken from the surroundings, the water, and the solution and its container quickly begin to feel cold.

Some of the cold packs used for treating sports injuries are made up of a bag of ammonium nitrate separated from a bag of water. When a person is injured, the contents of the bags are mixed together. The pack is then placed on the injury and the endothermic reaction 'freezes' the painful area. In other words, the reaction has taken heat out of the person's body.

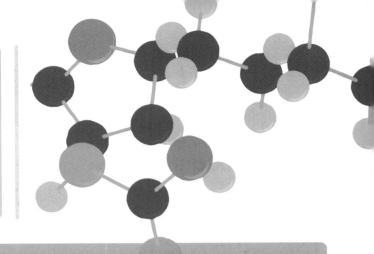

4 Work with a partner. Plan how you
would investigate the dissolving of the
following substances to see if they
caused an endothermic reaction.

a sodium chloride

b potassium chloride

Remember: You need to plan a fair test.

Review

Discuss the following list with a partner and decide if the statement is true or false.
Write down the number of any statement that you think is true and, when asked, hold
the number up for the rest of the class to see.

1 Chemical reactions that give out heat are called exothermic reactions.

2 Endothermic reactions give out heat and light.

3 Fuels burning are examples of endothermic reactions.

4 The reaction in an ice pack is an example of an endothermic reaction.

5 Combustion needs fuel, oxygen and ignition.

6 The Great Fire of London is an example of a giant exothermic reaction.

Chapter summary

In this chapter you have found out that:

- Some chemical reactions give out heat and are called exothermic.
- Burning methane and other fuels are exothermic reactions.
- The Great Fire of London was an exothermic reaction on a massive scale.
- Endothermic reactions require heat and take it from the surroundings.
- The reaction in an ice pack of ammonium nitrate and water is an example of an endothermic reaction.

Introduction

In this chapter we look at some of the positive and negative images of atoms.

- The splitting of atoms releases a great deal of energy called nuclear energy. The splitting process is called fission.
- Energy is also produced when atoms fuse together. This process is called fusion.
- Nuclear energy has been put to many uses including power stations and bombs.
- Radioactive materials can be hazardous but are also used safely in medicine and industry.
- Radioactive materials can remain hazardous for a very long time.

Write down five examples of where you have seen the word atom other than in science lessons. Share your list with a partner. Decide which examples show atoms in a positive light and which show them in a negative light.

The discoveries that have helped us to understand atomic structure have also allowed us to use the enormous energy held inside atoms to both build and destroy. As a result, there have been very mixed feelings about atoms during this, the atomic age. One thing is certain, though – the image of the atom has had a powerful impact on humankind.

In the 1950s Superman television serials and films were very popular. In search of a new villain, the writers invented Atom Man. This was Superman's arch-enemy Lex Luthor in disguise. Hardly fearsome to us today, Atom Man excited audiences with his ability to hurl flying saucers, kryptonite and nuclear missiles at Superman. Even more exciting, however, was his most brilliant invention. Using a special ray, Atom Man was able to break people down to their atoms and transport them across large distances. Once the atoms arrived they could be reassembled. Before Superman foiled his evil plans, Atom Man was able to use the ray to steal and kidnap.

Energy from the atom

The particles in the nucleus of atoms are held together by very strong forces. If the particles in the nucleus are disturbed then this releases a lot of energy. This can happen in one of two ways.

Fission

In some large atoms, such as plutonium and uranium, the nucleus may be unstable. If the nucleus is bombarded with a high-speed neutron then it can split into two parts. This releases a lot of energy, and some more neutrons. These neutrons can hit more nuclei, and so a chain reaction is set up.

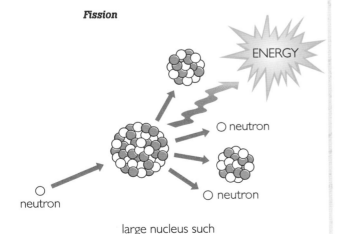

Fission

large nucleus such as uranium-235

Fusion

This happens naturally in the Sun and is the source of its energy. In fusion, two or more nuclei stick together. This process, which requires very high temperatures and pressures, causes a different element to be formed. In the Sun, two hydrogen nuclei are fused together to form a helium nucleus. Some of the mass of the hydrogen nuclei is lost and converted to energy.

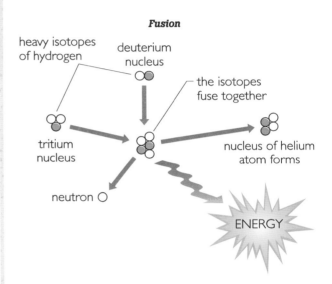

Fusion

Scientists can fuse hydrogen nuclei on a small scale, but the high costs and difficulty of arranging the high temperatures and pressures needed mean that at the moment fusion is only at the research stage. If the problems are ever overcome, then it will open up the way to unlimited, cheap and almost pollution-free energy.

The Manhattan Project

During the Second World War the United States started a top-secret project to try to use the energy of atoms as a weapon. In 1945 this project, known as The Manhattan Project, was violently successful. The first atomic bomb had been developed.

The project team, based in the New Mexico desert, first produced a test bomb known as 'Fat Boy'. On 16 July 1945, the first ever nuclear test took place. The test was given the codename Trinity and it was the start of the Atomic Age.

On 6 August 1945, the Enola Gay, an American B–29 bomber, took off on its flight to Hiroshima in Japan. It was carrying a 9000 pound atom bomb. Later that day the first atomic bomb to be used against people, nicknamed 'Little Boy', was dropped. The explosion was devastating and instantly killed over 60 000 people. Everything within a square kilometre of the explosion was turned to vapour. Slightly further out, buildings were totally destroyed, and even up to 5 kilometres away the city was ablaze. The atom bomb had used nuclear fission on a horrific scale.

Three days later a second target was selected. This was the Japanese town of Nagasaki. The population of 422 000 were carrying on with their normal lives when the bomb, nicknamed 'Fat Man', was dropped. Less than a second after the blast, nearly 40 000 people were dead.

President Truman summed it up well when he said:

> ❝The force from which the Sun draws its power has been loosed against those who brought war...❞
>
> **HARRY S. TRUMAN**

Devastation at Hiroshima.

3 Work with a partner. Answer the following questions and prepare to read out your answers to the rest of the class.

a Where was the first atom bomb developed?

b What was the nickname of the first test bomb?

c Which two Japanese cities were devastated by the first two nuclear weapons in history?

d How many people in total were killed instantly in the two explosions?

e What in your view are the rights and wrongs of dropping atomic bombs?

Harnessing the atom

The first nuclear reactor was built in 1942 by Enrico Fermi. Fermi was an Italian working at the University of Chicago and built his reactor in the squash court! Since then the use of nuclear power has grown, and now approximately 16 per cent of the world's energy is produced in this way.

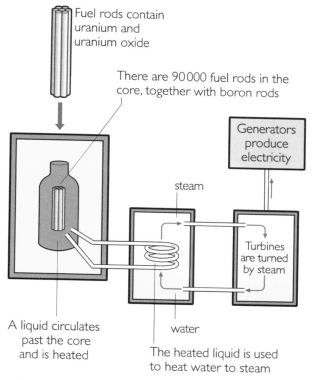

Fuel rods contain uranium and uranium oxide

There are 90 000 fuel rods in the core, together with boron rods

Generators produce electricity

steam

Turbines are turned by steam

A liquid circulates past the core and is heated

water

The heated liquid is used to heat water to steam

Plan of a nuclear power plant.

At the heart of a nuclear reactor is a core of fuel rods that contain uranium and uranium oxide. Fission reactions take place in these rods. Each fission reaction releases two or more neutrons, and, in a chain reaction, each neutron triggers another fission. To slow down and control the fission reactions, the fuel rods are mixed with rods made from boron. These absorb some of the neutrons.

Nuclear fission creates heat and this is used to change water into steam. In many respects, nuclear power stations are similar to those powered by fossil fuels such as gas, oil and coal. However, the fuel is very different.

Only 3 per cent of nuclear fuel cannot be recycled and used again. However, this 3 per cent is potentially very dangerous, as it is still radioactive. Some of the waste material can remain dangerously radioactive for over 24 000 years, so it has to be handled and stored very carefully. Much of the waste is stored as a concentrated liquid in stainless steel tanks. The tanks are covered in thick concrete for extra protection. The most radioactive water is turned into glass blocks. These are then placed in very deep mines.

4 Work with a small group. You are going to build a model that demonstrates how a nuclear power station works. Use the diagram to help you.

You will need:
- cardboard containers and tubes
- A4 paper
- glue
- adhesive tape
- marker pens
- scissors

This is what you do:

1 Use the diagram to help you to draw a plan

2 Use the card to make each of the structures needed

3 Place the structures together in the correct order

4 Label the model so that it forms a trail explaining the process

Chernobyl warning

The Chernobyl disaster resulted in the release of radioactive materials and the deaths of 31 people. Since 1986 there have been around ten further deaths due to cancer resulting from the accident. This case shows that there are risks linked to nuclear power, as well as potential benefits.

CHERNOBYL ACCIDENT

Nuclear Issues Briefing Paper   22 March 2001

The accident

On 25 April 1986, prior to a routine shut-down, the reactor crew at Chernobyl-4 began preparing for a test to determine how long turbines would spin and supply power following a loss of the main electrical power supply. Similar tests had already been carried out at Chernobyl and other plants, despite the fact that these reactors were known to be very unstable at low power settings.

Before the attempted test early on 26 April, there was a series of operator actions, which included disabling the automatic shutdown mechanisms. As the flow of coolant water diminished, power output increased. When the operator moved to shut down the reactor from its unstable condition arising from previous errors, a peculiarity of the design caused a dramatic power surge.

The fuel elements ruptured and the resultant explosive force of steam lifted off the cover plate of the reactor, releasing fission products into the atmosphere. A second explosion threw out fragments of burning fuel and graphite from the core and allowed air to rush in, causing the graphite moderator to burst into flames.

There is some dispute among experts about the character of this second explosion. The graphite burned for nine days, causing the main release of radioactivity into the environment.

---

5 Work with a partner on this extended activity.

  a Write down a series of questions relating to nuclear power that you would like to ask pro- and anti-nuclear organisations.

  b Research some pro- and anti-nuclear (www) organisations. You may wish to use the internet to search for these. Examples could include CND (Campaign for Nuclear Disarmament), Greenpeace, NIREX (Nuclear Industry Radioactive Waste Executive) and the United Kingdom Atomic Energy Authority.

  c Write to some of the organisations and ask them your questions.

  d Write a brief report describing the responses you receive.

Useful radioactivity

You may recall that radioactivity can be a product of some unstable nuclei which can break up and emit radiation. This is called radioactive decay. There are three types of radiation emitted during radioactive decay:

- Streams of alpha particles called alpha rays
- Streams of beta particles called beta rays
- Gamma rays

Radiation is harmful because it can damage cells and lead to cancers and other illnesses. However, radiation can be controlled and used. Examples include:

- Radiology – the use of X-rays in medicine
- Radiotherapy – using carefully controlled doses of radiation to kill cancer cells
- Radiocarbon dating – dating ancient artifacts using the breakdown of radioactive carbon

- Gamma radiography – using gamma rays to show what is happening in the body in a similar way to X-rays
- Radioactive tracing – using radioactive tracers to identify diseased organs

A specific example of using radiation in a positive way is in the preservation of food.

Approximately 25 to 30 per cent of foods harvested can be spoiled because of damage caused by microorganisms and insects. In a world where there is not enough food this is a very serious problem.

For thousands of years, people have treated foods to make them last longer, using techniques such as salting and drying. However, a more modern approach is now used in over 40 countries. This is irradiation and it is used on many kinds of food, ranging from spices, grains and grain products to fruit, vegetables and meat. Even astronauts eat foods preserved by irradiation.

6 Work with a small group. You will be allocated one of the uses of radiation. Your task is to research it in more detail.

www **a** Use the internet or other resources to find out about your topic.

b Make notes of your findings and print off any useful web resources.

c Write a one-page news item describing how radiation is used in your example.

d The pages can be collated to make a useful resource for the class.

Review

Divide the class into two teams. One team will role play being pro-nuclear energy, the other team will role play being anti-nuclear energy. Each team will be asked to respond to the following statements and give a scientific answer.

- Nuclear power would be unlimited, so we should use more of it.
- Fossil fuels produce greenhouse gases, so nuclear power is better.
- Nuclear waste lasts for thousands of years, so we should ban nuclear power.
- Nuclear power stations should be closed because they can explode and produce dangerous radiation.
- Radioactive materials are good as they have important medical uses.
- Nuclear power leads to nuclear weapons.

Chapter summary

In this chapter you have found out that:
- Atoms are used in science fiction films, books and magazines.
- The atom bomb has given atoms a bad reputation.
- Radioactivity is feared by many but radioactive materials can have valuable uses.
- Nuclear power can provide a great deal of the world's energy but can have disadvantages.

Answers

Explaining the world around us
P2 Q1
a Words may include atomic energy, atomiser, atom bomb, atomic explosion, atomic fuel

P6 Review
Leucippus.

Whether atoms were relatively large or very small.

10 million.

Lavoisier.

Beheaded on the guillotine.

Ideas about colour blindness, the atmosphere, gas pressure and atomic theory.

Particle theory and the states of matter
P8 Q1
a liquid

b gas

c solid

d liquid

e solid

P10 Q5
a Gases are easily compressed.

b The concrete is solid and will not compress and cushion the fall.

c The force of hitting the concrete surface would be so extreme it would damage bones and tissue.

d To cushion bumps in car and bicycle tyres.

e The gases (air) compress and cushion the bumps.

P11 Q6
a He could have added the gas to foods and measured how long they took to rot. He should have used similar samples of food in normal air as a control.

b He had observed the amusing effects on people, such as laughing.

c He realised that the gas worked to destroy pain.

d the gases may be poisonous, or make you act in an irresponsible way. It may also result in a shortage of oxygen.

P12 Review
Solid, liquid and gas.

Solid.

Gas.

The air is easily compressed and cushions the bumps.

The liquid water takes the shape of the container, but the cup stays the same shape because the particles can move more easily than the more fixed particles in the cup.

Heating and particles
P14 Q1
a By cooling the iron.

b The plastic would melt.

c It would melt and form liquid water and then evaporate to water vapour.

P17 Q4
a In the evaporator.

b In the condenser.

c Heat is taken from the room by the evaporator as it is used to change the liquid freon to gas.

P18 Q5
a The heat is being used to break bonds between water molecules and not to increase the temperature of the water.

P19 Q6
a Superheated steam is more reactive and will even react with steel.

b By heating water and then steam under pressure.

c Steel pipes and boilers could react with the steam and may even break.

P19 Q8
a The refrigerator.

b The ice is melting slowly.

c Liquid; liquids do not have a fixed shape.

P20 Review
Liquid.

They move further apart and eventually the solid may melt to give a liquid.

Freezing.

True.

It can react with steel pipes.

Freon.

Expansion and contraction
P22 Q1
a Brass.

b Oven glass.

c It expands less and will be less likely to crack when heated.

d Steel expands at almost the same rate and amount as concrete.

P23 Q2
a The sphere has expanded and is too big.

b The sphere will not fit through in any way; if it has only expanded upwards or sideways it might fit through if turned.

P23 Q3
a Alcohol

b The mercury does not stick to the sides of the thermometer.

c The temperature of molten steel is too high for both thermometers.

P25 Q5
a Examples may include in barometers and use in convection heating.

b Containers may explode.

c Gas particles are held less tightly than the particles in solids and liquids and are more able to move apart.

P26 Review
Liquids.

False – it is 1000 times.

The liquid expands and moves up the graduated tube.

No.

A bimetallic strip is made of strips of two different metals or alloys joined together. One of the metals expands further than the other and so, when heated, the strip will bend. This can be used to turn switches on and off, for example in a room thermostat.

The particles move further apart.

Uses include making barrels, putting metal rims on wheels, thermometers, rivets. Problems include cracking of glass and metal if repeatedly heated and cooled, and roads, railway lines and bridges buckling if they expand without expansion gaps.

Particles that make up air

P30 Q2
a So that there is no discomfort for passengers.
b The air pressure falls.
c There is less pressure outside than inside so the window will be pressed outwards.
d The air trapped in the middle ear can expand or contract and this can cause pain.

P30 Q3
a A low pressure area. Wet weather, moderate temperatures.
b Clear and cold.
c A band of cold air moving across an area.
d The wind will blow from an area of high pressure to an area of low pressure.

P31 Q5
a Air must be allowed into the can so that it can press onto the liquid.
b It is best to peel the edge of the sucker away and let air in. This makes the air pressure inside the sucker the same as on the outside, so it is no longer presses onto the wall.
c The damaged edges allow air to seep in.

P33 Q6
a A cofferdam is a box-like structure used to hold back water so work can be done inside it.
b Sometimes the cofferdam is not efficient enough – for example in very deep water.
c The compressed air increases the air pressure inside the caisson and this helps to keep the water out.
d 360 kilopascals. People cannot endure higher pressures.
e Little was known of 'the bends', a problem of nitrogen gas bubbling out of the blood as the workers moved too quickly from high-pressure air in the caisson to low-pressure air at the surface.

P33 Review
The atmosphere is the layer of air around the surface of the Earth. Climbers become breathless as they move to higher altitudes because the air is thinner.

By filling one balloon with more air than another and seeing if they balance on a see-saw.

This experiment showed that air pressure is very powerful and that a vacuum can be created and will persist.

A barometer is a device for measuring air pressure. It helps to predict the weather, since different air pressures help to drive the weather and we know which types of pressure brings certain weather patterns.

Examples include balloons, tyres, bouncy castles, drinking from straws.

Spreading out

P35 Q1
a The particles in a liquid are less tightly packed.
b Smoke in air - the air molecules move over greater distances than the water molecules.

c Brownian motion shows that particles are moving and colliding with each other.

P36 Q3
a They produce pheromones that diffuse through the air.

P37 Q4
a A substance that will dissolve in water or other named solvent.
b A liquid that will allow solutes to dissolve.
c Examples may include water, alcohol, nail varnish remover, white spirit.

P38 Review
The food chemicals diffuse across the room and humans have smell detectors in the nose.

The pheromones produced by the females diffuse through the air to the males.

The particles in the air slowly diffuse through tiny holes in the wall of the balloon.

The salt dissolves and spreads throughout the water.

The lumps have a larger volume, so much of the sugar is not in contact with the water. The grains are smaller and it is easier for molecules to come in contact with the water.

Making crystals

P41 Q2
a It is very hard.
b It is shiny and has interesting crystal shapes.
c Quartz is very tough and hard wearing, so rocks containing this material are also tough and hard wearing.

P42 Q3
a Talc is soft while quartz is very hard and would damage skin.
b Gypsum is soft and brittle.
c Yes, quartz is hardness 7 and fluorite is hardness 4.

P44 Review
A solution that will not allow any more solvent to dissolve.

By cooling of molten materials or from solutions of salts. Diamond.

Uses include gemstones, radios, radar, television, sandpapers, lenses.

Uses include flavouring foods, preserving foods, curing hides, feeding to livestock.

Particles and cells
All questions are research questions, or ones in which pupils design and share their information.

The atomic model after Dalton

P52 Q3
a Electrons: helium 2, carbon 6, oxygen 8, calcium 20.
b Protons: helium 2, carbon 6, oxygen 8, calcium 20.
c Neutrons: helium 2, carbon 6, oxygen 8, calcium 20.
d

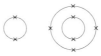

Helium   Carbon   Oxygen   Calcium

P53 Q4

a They wouldn't be hydrogen if they didn't have the same number of protons and electrons.

b Carbon dating is a method of finding out how old materials are by measuring how much of the carbon-14 isotope is left.

c Carbon-12 has 6 protons, 6 neutrons and 6 electrons. Carbon-14 has 6 protons, 8 neutrons and 6 electrons.

P53 Q5

a Over 200.

b Quarks.

c They allow scientists to split atoms into smaller and smaller particles in order to study them.

Elements, mixtures and compounds

P56 Q2

a Copper

b From 3000 to 2500 BCE.

c It is an alloy of two metals (copper and tin) and must be manufactured.

d Land of flames.

P57 Q3

a It would clash with hydrogen and be confusing.

b Ca.

c Sodium.

d Potassium.

How atoms combine

P61 Q1

Sodium: 2, 8, 1 electrons.
Oxygen: 2, 8, 6 electrons.
Neon: 2, 8 electrons.

a Neon

b Sodium: this atom only has to lose one outer electron.

P63 Q2

b magnesium: $Mg \rightarrow Mg^{2+} = +2$
lithium: $Li \rightarrow Li^{+} = +1$
fluorine: $F \rightarrow F^{-} = -1$
oxygen: $O \rightarrow O^{2-} = -2$

c Magnesium with fluorine or oxygen
Lithium with fluorine or oxygen

d Magnesium fluoride, magnesium oxide, lithium fluoride, lithium oxide.

P65 Q4

A: Na_2CO_3
B: Li_2O
C: $MgCl_2$

P66 Q5

a Water molecules are held together by hydrogen bonds.

b The hydrogen bonds form between the water molecules and the glass.

c The hydrogen bonds produce a surface tension on the water that acts as a very weak skin.

Atoms and patterns

P70 Q2

a Potassium.

b Gold.

c Gold, silver, copper.

d Potassium and sodium.

e Iron, zinc, aluminium and magnesium.

P73 Review

False; true; true; false; true; true.

Particles and chemical reactions

P74 Q1

a Reactants: hydrochloric acid and calcium.
Products: calcium chloride and hydrogen.

b Reactants: copper oxide and sulphuric acid.
Products: copper sulphate and water.

c Reactants: sodium and oxygen.
Products: sodium oxide.

P75 Q2

a Proteins are needed for growth and repair. Fats are needed for energy, insulation and for making membranes.

b Carbohydrates provide energy and fibre.

P77 Q5

a $CuO + 2HCl \rightarrow CuCl_2 + H_2O$

b $Zn + H_2SO_4 \rightarrow ZnSO_4 + H_2$

c $CaCO_3 + 2HCl \rightarrow CaCl_2 + CO_2 + H_2O$

P78 Review

Calcium chloride.
$CaCO_3 + 2HCl \rightarrow CaCl_2 + H_2O + CO_2$
Matter cannot be created or destroyed during a reaction.
Mutagens may have been produced and may cause a health hazard.
Examples may include atomic structure, flow of electricity, planetary motion, circuit diagrams.

Particles and energy

P80 Q2

a Butane.

b Wood.

c How easily it burns, the cost, how easy it is to handle and transport and pollution levels.

d Same diagram as methane but with petrol higher on the chart.

P82 Q3

a In the King's baker's house in Pudding Lane, possibly by a spark from the ovens.

b Wood.

c Heat and light.

d To reduce the amount of fuel (wooden houses) for the fire.

e It killed the plague-carrying rats.

f It lowers the temperature, removes oxygen and also dampens the fuel.

P83 Review

True; false; false; true; true; true.

The image of atoms

P86 Q3

a The New Mexico desert in the USA.

b Fat Boy.

c Hiroshima and Nagasaki.

d Over 100 000.

Index and glossary

Published by Letts Educational
The Chiswick Centre
414 Chiswick High Road
London W4 5TF
Telephone: 020 89963333
Fax: 020 87428390
E-mail: mail@lettsed.co.uk
Website: www.letts-education.com

Letts Educational is part of the Granada Learning Group. Granada Learning is a division of Granada plc.

All web addresses are correct at the time of going to press. The information in this book has been thoroughly researched and checked for accuracy. Safety advice is given where appropriate. Neither the authors nor the publishers can accept responsibility for any loss or damage incurred as a result of this book.

British Library Cataloguing in Publication Data
A catalogue record for this book is available from the British Library.

Produced by Hart McLeod, Cambridge
Commissioned by Helen Clark
Project management by Julia Swales
Editing by Pat Winter
Design by Bigtop Design, Bicester
Illustrations by Ken Vail Graphic Design and Jeff Edwards
Production by PDQ
Printed and bound in Italy

Acknowledgements
The publishers would like to thank the following for permission to use copyright material. Every effort has been made to trace copyright holders and to obtain their permission for the use of copyright material. The author and publishers will gladly receive information enabling them to rectify any error or omission in subsequent editions.

Text: p.11, Laughing gas, Ewan Cameron and Paul May, ©Ewan Cameron and Paul May; p.19, Melting point, Chubilicious, ©Cynthia; p.29, Air travellers to get better view, News in Science, reproduced by kind permission of ABC Science Online ©ABC Science Online www.abc.net/au/science/news/stories/s132484.htm; p.32, Caisson, Rudi Volti, ©Facts On File; p.48, Keeping Antarctic oil spills in check, News in Science, reproduced by kind permission of ABC Science Online ©ABC Science Online www.abc.net.au/science/news/stories/s531789.htm; p.58, Amalgams, Chem4Kids.com, reproduced by kind permission of Andrew Rader Studios, ©Andrew Rader Studios http://www.chem4kids.com; p.72, "Iron" by Roger McGough from Defying Gravity (Copyright ©Roger McGough 1992) is reproduced by permission of PFD (www.pfd.co.uk) on behalf of Roger McGough; p.75, Six Ways to Make Your Barbecues Healthier, extract from Danger on the BackyardGrill,©CBSnews.com www.cbsnews.com/ stories/2001/05/21/summer/main292536.shtml

Photos: p.6, ©Sheila Terry/Science Photo Library; p.8, ©Tony Craddock/Science Photo Library; p.10, ©Simon Grosset/Alamy; p.13, ©Maximillian Stock Ltd/Science Photo Library; p.29, ©Sheila Terry/Science Photo Library; p.40, ©Manfred Kage/Science Photo Library; p.68, ©Jonathan Blair/Corbis; p.70, ©Andrew Lambert Photography/Science Photo Library; p.78, ©Colin Cuthbert/Science Photo Library; p.84, ©SNAP (SYP)/Rex Features; p.86, ©Bettmann/Corbis